Up, Up and Away

East Yorkshire

Edited by Lucy Jeacock

C000226847

First published in Great Britain in 2000 by
YOUNG WRITERS
Remus House,
Coltsfoot Drive,
Peterborough, PE2 9JX
Telephone (01733) 890066

All Rights Reserved

Copyright Contributors 2000

HB ISBN 0 75432 296 3
SB ISBN 0 75432 297 1

FOREWORD

This year, the Young Writers' Up, Up & Away competition proudly presents a showcase of the best poetic talent from over 70,000 up-and-coming writers nationwide.

Successful in continuing our aim of promoting writing and creativity in children, our regional anthologies give a vivid insight into the thoughts, emotions and experiences of today's younger generation, displaying their inventive writing in its originality.

The thought, effort, imagination and hard work put into each poem impressed us all and again the task of editing proved challenging due to the quality of entries received, but was nevertheless enjoyable. We hope you are as pleased as we are with the final selection and that you continue to enjoy *Up, Up & Away East Yorkshire* for many years to come.

CONTENTS

Beverley Minster CE Primary School

Natalie Forrest	1
Charlotte Bussey	1
Emily Hunt	2
Allana Ross	2
Matthew Molson	3
Hamzah Butt	3
Josh Meredith	4
Kerrin Tatman	4
Hayley Sims	5
Jessica Bailey	6
Naomi Reynolds	6
Ruth Thompson	7
Jordan Clark	7
Matthew Daniel	8
Alex Rossi	8
Laura Gray	9
Alice Ramsay	9
Joanne Overton	9
Bronwyn Ellis	10
Emma Dennison	10
Sophie Whittaker	11
Amber Bryant	12
Davy Clark	12
Victoria Barley	13
Phillip Hargreaves	13
Zarah Mukalaf	14
Camilla Stead	14
Tom Matthews	15
Amy Parkin	16
Katie Clark	16
Emma Coggins	17
Shashank Srirama	17
Steven Parkinson	18
Christie Basile	18
Tom Beckley	19

Joe Oldroyd   20
Rosie Bristow   20
Jessica Horner   21
Joe Thompson   21
Vikki Watson   22
Esther Seaman   23
Amy Allinson   24
David Hickling   25
Sarah Gibbins   26

Buckingham Primary School
Christopher Neylon   26
Nathan Gardner   27
Matthew Shaw   27
Laura Knight   28
David Taylor   29
Emma Louise McNamara   30
Matthew Clayton   30
Peter Abram   31
Carla Taylor   32
Karl Brook   33

Chiltern Primary School
Ricky Braithwaite   33
Rachel Fee   34
Melanie Roberts   34
Katie Moody   35
Jamie Stainforth   35
Christine Griffin   36
Sara Wiltshire   36
Cara Fox   37
Kimberley Price   37
David Blake   38
Carl Sonley   39
Leah Calderwood   39
Liam Rust   40
Matthew Gallagher   40
Simon Ireland   41

Cheryl Christensen 41
Victoria Williams 41
Nicholas Dunhill 42
Sarah Windley 42
Christopher Lyon 43
Patrick Bywood 43
Samantha Sheppard 43
Joshua Hood 44
Alex Gallagher 44
Joshua Mills 44
Ross McCoid 45
Ella Wood 45
Leah Beauchamp 46
Alicia McKinney-Anderson 46
Debbie Mawer 47
Danielle Welsh 47
Katie Tordoff 48
Sarah Brown 48
Larrissa Wolton 49
Dean Hobson-Campbell 49
James Lowe 50
Rikki Harrison 50

Clifton Primary School
Kelsie Carter 51
Adam Douglas 51
Hayley Munro 52
Chelsea Sparrow 52
Zoe Craddock 53
Callum Turner 53
Kelly Barton 54
Natalie Evans 54
Rachel Hargreaves 54
Sonya Morgan 55

Cowick Primary School
Helen Abbott 55
Katrina Barker 56

Matthew Carey	56
Amie Louise Henderson	57
Geraldine Buckley	58
Chloe Waterson	59
Willis Hall	60

Estcourt Primary School

Shaun Bexley	60
Leigh Tomlinson	61
Scott Walsh	62
Louis Suddaby	62
Gareth Jones	63
Robert Anderson	63
Robert Shiels	64
Samuel McDonald	64
Christopher Mansfield	65
Andrew Isle	65
Laura Waslin	66
Matthew Parker	66
Michael Anderson	67
Scott Sharlotte	68
Ricky F Sheriff	68
Danielle Cooper	69
Grace Nicholson	70
Ashlea Claffey	71
Nikki Parker	72
Stacie Reffin	72
Sarah Ockelton	73

Hornsea Community Primary School

Ashley Bland	73
James Bowman	74
Andrew Walker	74
Callum Thompson	75
Richard Oates	75
Hannah McNeil	76
Aaron Dawick	76
Freyja Fitzpatrick-Hilditch	77

Anneiga Drage 77
David Simpson 78
Bruce Ridley 79
Mark Embleton 80
Kieran J McBeth 80
Victoria Bishop 81
Lisa Lambert 81
Hannah Lawson 82
Karen Symonds-Tate 82
Rachel Rhodes 83
Amanda Smith 83
Becky Rhodes 84
Pip Dove 84
Kirsty Clegg 85
Jack Billam 86
Jonathan Worsdale 87

Kellington Primary School
Samantha Watson 87
Laura Evans-Booth 88
Ellie Robinson 89
Daniel Baker 90
Tim Addy 90
Gemma Reeson 91
Stephen Gudgeon 92
Luke Bednall 93
Amy Winter 94

St Mary's & St Joseph's RC Primary School
Tim Russell 94
Rory Tipping 95
Jennifer Hughes 96
James Hepburn 96
Heather Plimmer 97
Jessica Forbester 98
Ellie Holbrough 98
Olivia Brown 99
Edward Walker 99

Mitchell Scollen	100
Stacey Richardson	100
Claire Hancock	101
Ben Forbester	101
Emma Russell	102
Rebecca Cusack	102
Michael Richardson	103
Angela Coffey	103
Shonagh Hepburn	104
Elizabeth-Anne Coffey	104
Joel Saltmer	105
Araminta Rowlatt	106
Philip Marshall	106
Joanna Smith	107
Jonathan Cusack	107
Lindsey Hoyle	108
Charlotte Linsley	108
Leanne Vere	109
Jinny Hardy	109
Kieran Anderson	110
Gabrielle Jones	111
Alexander Brown	112

St Vincent's RC Primary School

James Meadowcroft	113
Natasha Todd	113
Christopher Dixon	113
Jack Burnham	114
Jack Oyston	114
Annie Wykes	115
Ross Walker	115
Charlotte Stather	116
Lauren Lambert	116
Andrew Murray	117
Natalie Hinchsliff	117
Callum Sweeting	118
Louis Ramsay	118
Lizzy Butler	119

Lizzy Currie	120
Jacinta Insole	121
Etta Hawksworth	122
Jacinta Hickson	122
Molly Mangan	123
Eleanor Leach	124
Holly Caprani	124
Emily Watson	125
Ben Dawson	126
Nathan Caprani	126
Hannah Loader	127
Joe Mellors	128
Jack Williamson	128
Mike Naama	129
Mark Richardson	129
Max Brown	130
Sarah Marsden	130
Antony Good	131
Lucy Stephens	131
Thomas Watson	132
Katherine Gregory	132
Joshua Burley	133
George Mangan	134
Alexander Wood	134
Paul Naama	135
Naomi Watson	135
Abbie Walton	136
Joseph Gateshill	136
Corin France	137
Suzanne Deyes	138
Sophie Kavallares Simpson	138
Samantha Vizor	139
Reuben Seetal	140
Daniel Haigh	141
Amy Dakin	141
Stephanie Thompson	142

Melissa O'Connell	142
Caroline Fish	143
James Butler	143
David Smith	144

Stockwell Primary School

Natasha Dennison	145
John Carr	145
Emma Chapman	145
Sophie Johnson	146
Chelsea Dent	146
Melanie Roberts	147
Shane Gorbutt	147
Jade Priestman	148
Natalie Clarke	148
John Esders	149
Gregg Blanchard	149
Kay Taylor	150
Thomas Dervey	150
Emma Louise Bones	150
Wendy Whisker	151
Daniel Green	151
Chloe Arnold	151

Stoneferry Primary School

Laura Foster	152
Sarah Cooke	152
Leanne Smith	153
Louise Thomas	154
Bethany Sharp	154
Stephanie Lyth	155
Simon Johnson	156
Jamie Morfitt	156
Jenny Jones	157

Sutton Park Primary School

Frances Suzette Ellis	158
Annie Woodcock	159
Marlie-Rae Willerton	159
Katie Athorn & Louise Vernon	160
Kayleigh Prest	160
Kelly Robinson	161
Hannah Fennell	161
Laura Green	162
Sasha Collinson	162
Lee Williams	163
Laura Firth	163
Sarah Capes	164
Lewis Moffat	164
Amy Sharpless	165
Kelly Armett	166
Lauren C Brown	166
Samantha Langdale	167
Heidi Malton	168
Sarah Myers	169

Tilbury Primary School

Katie Mattinson	170
Stephanie Cox	170
Josh Daw	171
Elisha Smith	171
Alicia Black	172
Ashley Calver	172
Joseph Rowbottom	173

The Poems

UP, UP AND AWAY

Up, up and away in a red and yellow balloon,
Hair flowing like a stream.
Stars singing, birds flying,
Clouds blowing through the air.
People having fun!
A red and yellow balloon, babies crying too.
I am flying in the air, rabbits crouching,
Having lots of fun.
I am flying in the air,
Mum and Dad are being fair,
Bumper crops are too.
I am flying in the air
Having lots and lots of fun.
I am flying in the air!

Natalie Forrest (8)
Beverley Minster CE Primary School

IT'S

An arrow mover
A screen saver
A wall hopper
A trap keeper
A cat peeper
A hole in the wall
A tall an' all
A sensitive whisker
A food nicker
A little house
It's a . . .
        Mouse.

Charlotte Bussey (10)
Beverley Minster CE Primary School

1

UP, UP AND AWAY

Here I am stranded, wind whooshing through my hair,
Flying up high in the air.
Ground so small, tiny as a shrew,
I really can't see you.
Wondering what you're doing,
You might be out, you might be in.
Fire keeps the balloon going,
I bet the river is definitely flowing.
So here I am flying about,
Suddenly birds start to shout.
I wonder what it is like down there,
I wouldn't jump, I wouldn't dare.
Hours gone by, I say to Mum 'Hi,'
Now I'm back home sweet home.

Emily Hunt (8)
Beverley Minster CE Primary School

UP, UP AND AWAY

Up, up and away in a red balloon,
Flying softly in the air, round the sun and moon.
People so small on the ground,
Tiny houses as well, all around.
The balloon is blown about here and there and everywhere,
All the adventures you can have in a balloon is unbelievable.
Have a ride, go round the clouds,
Get on the balloon!

Allana Ross (8)
Beverley Minster CE Primary School

ROBOT!

Deep in space where the robot lies
Spinning around where the UFO flies.

The robot who was made to use
Is no good when it blows its fuse.

Robots flying around in space
Most people call it an unusual place.

Zooming around looking for more parts
Wondering where the robot race starts.

The robot race takes place each year
And is entered by robots with a fear
Of exploding by drinking beer.

The robot he won the race
And took the cup back into space.

Matthew Molson (10)
Beverley Minster CE Primary School

WAR

War is dark black and grey like thunder and lightning,
It smells like deadly gas that makes you choke,
It tastes like rotting flesh in a basement that's been
            rotting for centuries.
It sounds like skeletons screaming and screeching in
            a graveyard,
War feels as if you are being terribly tortured,
War lives in the darkest corner at the edge of the Earth.

Hamzah Butt (10)
Beverley Minster CE Primary School

MY DAD

My dad has time
To talk to my mum
To drink his tea
But never has time
To play with me

My dad has time
To get a shower
To play football
With my brother
To pay the fee
But never has time
To play with me

And still has time
To do his work
To drive his car
To jump off a cliff
And shout the word
Weeee
But never has time
To play with *meeee*

Josh Meredith (9)
Beverley Minster CE Primary School

BUGS!

Bugs! Bugs!
They're everywhere,
Some in the garden, some in your hair!

Bugs! Bugs!
You'll never guess,
They're all over the place and are quite a pest!

Bugs! Bugs!
They'll give you a fright,
Bed bugs will scare you at past midnight!

Bugs! Bugs!
They make you itch,
All over your body,
Until you twitch!

Kerrin Tatman (9)
Beverley Minster CE Primary School

HULL FC

The season arrives,
Going to beat all the teams,
Away and at home.

All the players come on,
Stanley Gene scores a great try,
The end 27-12.

All the fans scream, shout,
Stanley Gene scores a hat-trick,
The players run about.

Hull FC, the best,
They can beat all the best teams,
Such as Halifax.

New season begins
Black and stripes come out,
Halifax beware!

Hull FC are the best,
They can beat the rest,
They can beat Castleford Tigers.

Hayley Sims (10)
Beverley Minster CE Primary School

THE SCHOOL MONSTER

A maths muncher
A number cruncher.

A science swallower
A force follower.

An English eater
A dictionary defeater.

A history haunter
A Tudor taunter.

An art attacker
A paintbrush whacker.

A PE pusher
A football crusher.

Makes the school monster most terrifying.

Jessica Bailey (10)
Beverley Minster CE Primary School

UP, UP AND AWAY

I went to the shops with my teddy bear
I bought some balloons
I blew up the balloons
Then tied them to my bear
He went up, up and away
Floating in the air.

Naomi Reynolds (8)
Beverley Minster CE Primary School

GUINEA PIGS

Guinea pigs are such lazy things,
They cannot fly, they have no wings,
They cannot gallop like a horse
And they only eat their *second* course.

Guinea pigs are such lazy things,
They cannot swim, they have no fins,
They aren't as adventurous as sheep,
Because they only run, hide, then peep.

Guinea pigs are such lazy things,
They never hang around your bins,
You always find them in one place,
That's always quiet and very safe.

Guinea pigs are so lazy,
They could be as still as a daisy,
But guinea pigs are the best pets for me,
Because I'm as lazy as could be!

Ruth Thompson (10)
Beverley Minster CE Primary School

WAR

War is the colour of blood,
It smells of horrendous dead bodies,
It tastes villainous,
It sounds like the wind blowing away
from the battlefield,
It feels like a phantom haunting you every hour,
It lives in the heart of a battlefield.

Jordan Clark (10)
Beverley Minster CE Primary School

UNDER THE SEA

U nder the sea there is lots to see
N ot a lot there will give you a scare
D eep under the sea are lots of creatures
E els and seals swim around looking for meals
R ays of moonlight appear at night.

T he sea is covered with rocks and rubble
H idden gold and secret caves are all hiding from us
E verything there has a home.

S oggy seaweed, sticks to the rocks
E verything sleeps during night but in the morning all is bright
A ferry passes overhead, while all the fish have gone to bed.

Matthew Daniel (9)
Beverley Minster CE Primary School

UP, UP AND AWAY

Different colours flying above our heads,
The giant hot air balloon starts its travels.
It will travel high and wide fuelled by the wind,
Passing through lots of countries.
Look to the left, see the pretty Indian girls
Dancing in their colourful saris.
To the right, see the African girls
Dancing in their costumes.
Let's continue our journey high up above the sky,
Watching the world go by.

Alex Rossi (8)
Beverley Minster CE Primary School

HAPPINESS

Happiness is as yellow as the sand, whooshing in from the sea,
It smells like sweet strawberries, growing in a beautiful garden.
It tastes like a creamy ice-cream, when it's dripping down your arm,
It sounds like a child laughing, when having fun in a river or stream.
It feels like the water splashing at your feet in the swimming pool,
It lives in the heart of the sun, smiling with happiness.

Laura Gray (9)
Beverley Minster CE Primary School

HOPE

Hope is as white as snow with the sun shining down
It smells like the sweetest rose in a beautiful garden,
Hope tastes like the tastiest gingerbread man,
It sounds like water trickling down rocks in a waterfall,
It feels like the fur on your ted in bed at night,
Hope lives in the bottom of your heart.

Alice Ramsay (10)
Beverley Minster CE Primary School

FEAR

Fear is black like broken rubble,
It smells like mice and rats,
It tastes like mouldy bread,
It sounds like horror and screaming,
Fear feels like a hole in the bottom of your heart,
It lives in a faraway world with anger and hatred.

Joanne Overton (10)
Beverley Minster CE Primary School

SPRING

Spring is here, there's nothing to fear,
The snowdrops are beginning to flower,
The sky has cleared its foggy beard
And the birds are taking a shower.

It's a new beginning not an end
New creatures are born, children make friends.
The lambs are springing,
New birds are singing.
Foals are stamping in their barn
And piglets are oinking on the farm.

I can see lovely rows of daffodils
Spreading over the open fields and hills.

Oh I do love
Spring, spring, spring!

Bronwyn Ellis (8)
Beverley Minster CE Primary School

UP, UP AND AWAY

Once I was up there in the sky,
Up, up and away in the air I did fly,
In the sunny warm weather,
Looking down on the heather,
In the fields down low,
Flying peacefully slow.
At first I didn't want to go on,
Next minute I was swaying along,
I feel so light,
What a wonderful flight!

Emma Dennison (8)
Beverley Minster CE Primary School

A

Trouble maker
Window breaker

Milk stealer
Card dealer

Bird killer
Chair sitter

Fur dropper
Door stopper

Present leaver
Night diva

Fish eater
Belly heater

Morning waker
Leaf raker

Food beggar
Ground digger

All these things
Lead to my . . .

Sophie Whittaker (10)
Beverley Minster CE Primary School

DOGS

Dogs awake at day
starting to play
howling away
eating their food
don't run
because dogs run
as fast as a gun
pouncing around
lying on the ground
messing around
then at night
they go to sleep
they don't give a peep
till the next day.

Amber Bryant (9)
Beverley Minster CE Primary School

WISHFUL THINKING

I am not a very good poet
But I really think I owe it
To do my very best
And maybe beat the rest.
To just win this competition
I already have a vision
It's Miss Hardwick saying 'Clark
You deserve the highest mark.
I just can't believe my eyes
You have won that special prize.'

Davy Clark (9)
Beverley Minster CE Primary School

DEAR GRANDMA

Dear Grandma,
    While you were gone
    A mysterious handprint popped up
    In the velvet curtains.
    The goldfish seems to have eaten the cake
    That you made for the village fete.
    A series of plates dislodged themselves
    And fell on the floor.
    Pop's walking stick managed to snap into two,
    Some of the bed springs sprung
    And I know you shall be rather mad . . .
    So I've gone to live with Uncle Sinbad!

            From Tori
                X X X

Victoria Barley (11)
Beverley Minster CE Primary School

WAR

War is like demons' blood,
It tastes like burnt, bitter bones,
It sounds like bombing the burning buildings
And gunpowder.
It smells like black, horrible, steamy smoke
And rats' breath.
It feels like evil spirits coming back
From a lifeless grave.
It lives in the battlefield floor.

Phillip Hargreaves (10)
Beverley Minster CE Primary School

EVERYBODY'S FRIEND

My name is Zarah M,
In May I will be ten.
I can't wait until then,
I will have a party
And along will come Ken.
Although he is rather old,
He has a heart of gold,
I think he's rather nifty,
Even though he's over fifty.
He is rather nice,
(But not like me, made of sugar and spice!)
Sometimes he can be mad,
But I have to put up with him,
Because he's a friend of my dad.
Now I'm getting to the end,
I have to say Ken's everybody's friend.
He's happy, jolly and hearty,
So I will invite him to my party.

Zarah Mukalaf (9)
Beverley Minster CE Primary School

FEAR

Fear is as black as a witch's cloak,
Swaying in the moonlit sky.
Fear smells like a deadly gas,
It tastes like mouldy, smelly cheese,
It sounds like people creeping up on you
In the middle of the dark night.
It feels like a cold polar bear lost in the snow,
Fear lives at the bottom of the dark sea.

Camilla Stead (10)
Beverley Minster CE Primary School

UP, UP AND AWAY

A hot air balloon
In lots of different colours
Went high into the sky
Reaching up to the moon
Up, up and away.

A big noisy plane
Carrying lots of holidaymakers
Took off from the airport
Just like a computer game
Up, up and away.

A lovely little bird
Singing loudly in the tree
Spotted the local cat
And after that nothing was heard
Up, up and away.

A gentle little butterfly
Sitting on the summer flowers
Waggled its wings in the sun
And took off into the sky
Up, up and away.

Tom Matthews (9)
Beverley Minster CE Primary School

DAY TO NIGHT

Day
Ending,
Sun descends.
Hazy colours
Fill the horizon.
Soft clouds of every hue
Stretch their arms across the sky.
Creatures run to woods and burrows,
Owls hoot their words of warning.
Darkness casts its shadow.
Not a noise is heard,
Earth is waiting -
Silent, still -
For the
Night.

Amy Parkin (10)
Beverley Minster CE Primary School

UP, UP AND AWAY

Up, up in the sky
I can see a butterfly.
Down, down on the ground
I can see something round.

As I ascend,
Place your eyes on me,
As I go over the horizon
I am in my hot air balloon,
I may just manage to touch the moon.

Katie Clark (9)
Beverley Minster CE Primary School

THE TELL-TALE

I have seen it, seen it all before,
There is a creature that lives under the floor.

He's big and furry and hairy too
And he's bigger, much bigger than you.

He's really scary, he's like a bear
And he is not mentioned, he's very rare.

At night he comes in your house,
He tries to be quiet, quiet as a mouse.

He gave my dog a disease,
And his favourite dinner is cheese.

The floor creaks at midnight,
He's so scary he can give you a fright.

At daytime he just rests,
But I think this creature is the *best!*

Emma Coggins (9)
Beverley Minster CE Primary School

HAPPINESS

Happiness is as pink as the petals of a rose,
It smells like the sweet smell of bluebells in a field.
Happiness tastes of sweet sugar,
It sounds like a bird singing on a branch,
It feels soft and cuddly.
Happiness lives in the heart of a green, grassy meadow.

Shashank Srirama (10)
Beverley Minster CE Primary School

UP, UP AND AWAY

One sunny day I saw a balloon in the sky
As high as the birds can fly
I saw some people looking out
I wondered if they could hear me shout.

The balloon floats on the gentle breeze
It glides among the clouds with the greatest of ease
When it's in the air it makes no sound
But it makes a bump when it hits the ground.

When I close my eyes I think I'm there
Way up high in the air.
Sometimes when I look down
I see a circus with a funny clown.

When I open my eyes, I'm not in the balloon
But I hope I will be, very, very soon
When I go back and look to the sky
I still see the balloon flying high.

Steven Parkinson (9)
Beverley Minster CE Primary School

DRAGON

In the darkness of the night came the smell of Hell,
Flying fiercely through the sky came a shadow
As big as an eye-catching eagle!
A gush of wind came rushing through,
A few minutes after the shadow had gone through.
Eyes as big as a head, jaws as big as a leg.
Fire-breathing, hot smoke, breath smells of Coke.
Tail swaying, waving through,
Banging buildings down, your house too.

Christie Basile (10)
Beverley Minster CE Primary School

UP, UP AND AWAY

Last summer we went on holiday,
We flew to Barbados on a big jet plane,
The plane took off at Manchester airport,
It was pouring with rain.

The captain said 'Fasten your seat belts,
Until the light goes out,'
The plane took off very fast,
Dad said 'We'll soon be there no doubt.'

The plane was flying through the clouds,
We were so very high,
Out of the window I saw Ireland,
Then I waved it goodbye.

The plane was full of people,
But you could walk up and down between the seats,
The lady brought the food on a special tray
And then I ate my sweets.

Our journey started in England,
We flew up, up and away,
The plane came in to land over the bright blue sea
And we saw Barbados Bay.

Tom Beckley (9)
Beverley Minster CE Primary School

UP, UP AND AWAY

Before the ride I felt a bit bad
But just then I felt glad
I felt a bit nervous
But then up, up away,
Up into the sky
Near to the clouds
And where the birds fly.
There it was, The Grand Canyon
What a sight to see
In a helicopter, how lucky for me.
Sweeping and swooping through the clouds
But before long it's time to go back
Slowly down onto the tarmac.

Joe Oldroyd (8)
Beverley Minster CE Primary School

HAPPINESS

Happiness is a beautiful yellow like the sunflowers in the garden.
Happiness is like the smell of toasting bread wafting up the stairs.
Happiness tastes like sugar mice, lemonade and a party picnic
with cake.
Happiness sounds like rattling pencil cases, crackling fires
and choirs singing happy songs.
Happiness feels like a soft feather bed, warm pyjamas, a bubbly
bath.
Happiness lives all over the world in good people's hearts.

Rosie Bristow (9)
Beverley Minster CE Primary School

Up, Up And Away

Up, up and away in a hot air balloon
I'd like to go up in one very soon
To float around in the sky
To see the world from up on high.

To climb into the balloon's basket
That would be really fantastic
To leave the ground
Would make my heart pound.

To float up into the clouds
Would make me very proud
Up, up and away
I wonder if it will happen one day?

Jessica Horner (8)
Beverley Minster CE Primary School

Sports

Football is my favourite sport
I play the rules that I've been taught
It is a game for girls and boys
When they get bored with their toys

Basketball is my favourite sport
With lots of teams we have fought
To be the champions of the game
Bring home the cup and have lots of fame

Tennis is my favourite sport
We play on a very grassy court
Racquets, balls and tennis shoes
Nobody ever likes to lose.

Joe Thompson (8)
Beverley Minster CE Primary School

WHAT AM I?

Drip drop,
Pitter patter,
Splash gurgle,
Plop.
Ping pong,
Trickle tinkle,
Tip tap,
Whoosh.

Splash sprinkle,
Spray squirt,
Showery drizzly,
Soaking wet.
Damp moist,
Sticky sweaty,
Soak drenched,
Drown.

Flood spill,
Overflow leak,

What am I?

Ooze seep.
Drip trickle,
Dribble pour,
Stream drain,
Surge.

Have you guessed it yet?
Yes it's
            Water.

Vikki Watson (11)
Beverley Minster CE Primary School

THE DRAGON

Fiery smoke flooding out from the car-sized lungs
Jutting teeth, razor-blade sharp,
Breath that is half the smell of Hell,
Massive claws, the size of a horse.
Big sleek body, lightning quick reactions,
Grabbing claws that tear like saws.
Swishing swooshing tail, with a blow like the devil,
Never-tired wings beating the air like Thor's hammer,
They could destroy a thousand castles.
Ever-glinting eyes with a centre like fire,
Flying like a monster way back from the ages.
Casting a shadow that turns day into night,
Flying west from her nest but not for too long
Or the eggs will be gone.
Egg stealers, egg catchers,
The dragon is fierce, the dragon is frightening,
Fire suffocating the villages and towns.
Flames leaping high from the jaws,
Licking at the creature's claws.
Blazer was the name of that ferocious dragon,
Claws glinting like gold, he is only 10cm tall
And I'm taking him to bed with me,
He's my favourite toy.

Esther Seaman (9)
Beverley Minster CE Primary School

WHAT IS . . . A STAR

A star is a frosty tree,
In space.

A star is a white Smartie,
On dark chocolate.

A star is a chalk smudge,
On a blackboard.

A star is the moon,
In the blue sky.

A star is a shell,
In the ocean.

A star is a ball of wool,
Hanging from the sky.

A star is a white button,
On a black coat.

A star is a white table,
In a black room.

A star is an ice cube,
In a box.

A star is a white seed,
In the soil.

Amy Allinson (10)
Beverley Minster CE Primary School

INSIDE MY HEAD

I am supposed to write a poem
Of what I think inside my head,
But there's just one little problem,
I don't know what to put,
So I am writing all this down
Because I have no inspiration,
But look this is the idea in my head,
So my inspiration isn't dead.

My thinking box is growing,
I am seeing colours inside my head,
Flying away from planet Earth,
My inspiration isn't dead.

Past Proxima Centauri,
Four point two light years from this Earth,
My thinking box is growing,
Young stars are giving birth.

Little baby stars are growing,
Inventing families of their own.
My thinking box is growing,
My mind has definitely grown.

Past the other side of the Milky Way,
I don't know what to say.
My thinking box is growing,
Hip, hip, hip, hip, hooray.

David Hickling (11)
Beverley Minster CE Primary School

IT'S A

Long tail
squeaky wail.

Fat lump
very plump.

Huge teeth
grabbing 'thief'.

Very hairy
bit scary.

Bin scavenger
sewage scrapper.

Dinner for cat
it's a . . .

Sarah Gibbins (11)
Beverley Minster CE Primary School

RUGBY LEAGUE

R   is for roughness,
U   is for Union,
G   is for grim sights on the pitch,
B   is for the big boys that the game is for,
Y   is for youngsters in winning teams.

L   is for a line out to the team,
E   is for every argument with the referee,
A   is for an ace ball that always gets a goal,
G   is for a grubber that goes along the ground,
U   is for under 11s that are the best,
E   is for entertainment that is super.

Christopher Neylon (10)
Buckingham Primary School

THE BOY WHO WAS ADDICTED TO THE TV

I'm addicted to the TV
I take it to school
I even take it on the loo with me
And I take it to bed.
Now my eyes are square
It's hard to watch the TV
So I had a fight with the TV
But it fell down the stairs
So I took it to the hospital
To have it x-rayed
All it was, was a dislocated aerial
So I had it repaired.

Nathan Gardner (10)
Buckingham Primary School

SCHOOL DINNERS

School dinners are not the best,
The cooks are a mess.
If I was a doctor
I would make them
Have some tests.
The mash is like mud,
The spaghetti is like worms,
The sweetcorn is like teeth.
When I have finished eating,
My stomach starts to churn,
My legs begin to wobble,
My heart begins to burn.
Please Mum don't make me stay,
Because my stomach has just busted.

Matthew Shaw (11)
Buckingham Primary School

BROTHERS

My brother David, is tall and thin,
Almost like a rolling pin,
He's very funny and makes me laugh,
Even when I have to have a bath.

He's sometimes silly and sometimes not,
He buys me sweets, quite a lot,
He sometimes picks me up from school
And takes me to the swimming pool.

He likes a drink or so we think,
And then closes his eye in a wink.
He sometimes acts like a clown,
So then I give him a very big frown.

Sometimes though, he tends to forget,
My birthday which makes me upset,
But then he tells me he's only pretending,
And gives me a present which needed sending.

He makes me laugh, he makes me smile
And then you see for a quite a while
What makes him my special friend,
He's the best brother in the world.

Laura Knight (10)
Buckingham Primary School

FOOD, GLORIOUS FOOD

Doughnuts, doughnuts big and small,
Doughnuts, doughnuts golden brown.
Doughnuts, doughnuts different fillings,
Doughnuts, doughnuts with sugary tops.

Chocolate cakes, chocolate cakes smothered in chocolate,
Chocolate cakes, chocolate cakes with a creamy filling.
Chocolate cakes, chocolate cakes with cherries on top,
Chocolate cakes, chocolate cakes with icing sugar on top.

Galaxy, Galaxy melts in your mouth,
Galaxy, Galaxy, rip the wrapper off.
Galaxy, Galaxy, eat it all down,
Galaxy, Galaxy is so sweet.

Cauliflower, cauliflower, lumpy white,
Cauliflower, cauliflower, I look and balk.
Cauliflower, cauliflower is very rubbery,
Cauliflower, cauliflower is rather soggy.

Give me chocolate any day!

David Taylor (11)
Buckingham Primary School

MY TEACHER

My teacher is nice
My teacher keeps mice
My teacher is a princess
With long golden hair
She rules the class like she doesn't care
Her jewels are like stars
And ice-blue eyes that twinkle
When she laughs her face crinkles
Her house is like a mansion
She's into fashion
She has a pet lion
That tries to defy her
The class is spotless when she's here
But, when she's off
She still comes to school
And gives us the flu!

Emma Louise McNamara (11)
Buckingham Primary School

MY FAMILY

My dad is a leopard running through the trees
My mam is a fish swimming through the white blue sea
My brother is an alligator in the shallow water
Waiting for his prey
My cousin is a monkey swinging through the trees
My friend is a cheetah running so quick
My uncle is a sloth, so lazy and sleepy
And never gets up
My auntie is a parrot, always chattering on
And that is my family.

Matthew Clayton (10)
Buckingham Primary School

MY FRIEND

I look at him but you just have to laugh,
I think he is an alien.
I think the mother ship is coming for him,
He comes to school in green slime.
The only things my teacher can say is
'Wipe your nose before it is too late.'
He is the only one who eats his school dinner,
I think he is made out of it.
He melts on the playground on a sunny day,
All that is left is green slime.
I have been to his house, once,
I was sucked up in a flash.
When I got out I found out that he was wanted
In all of England.
One day some men in black,
Came and said, 'Do you know an alien?'
'Yes,' I said
'Not now,' said the men
'Look in the light please,'
Flash!

Peter Abram (11)
Buckingham Primary School

MY SISTER

My sister is pretty,
My sister is kind,
Sometimes she drives me out of my mind.
We get our pocket money on a Saturday,
She spends hers on sweets,
Then when she runs out,
Mum makes me give her my treats.
My sister likes to read Winnie the Pooh,
Sometimes likes to draw it too.
Every night she counts sheep,
Most of all I cannot get to sleep.
Her best friend is Lisa,
They like to eat pizza.
My sister is very lazy,
Sometimes she can be crazy.
She likes to go swimming a lot,
But when she gets in the pool she stays in one spot.
She likes to eat Cadbury's Creme Eggs,
But most of all I love her.
She's like a cuddly teddy bear
And that's my sister.

Carla Taylor (11)
Buckingham Primary School

SPACE

Space, space
A weird place
Somewhere to go
And somewhere to stay
Maybe one day
I will have a
New race
As I go into outer space
But when I noticed that I bought
A lottery ticket
I had won and
I started to play cricket
Cricket was fun
Hitting the moon
Against the sun
Space set on fire
Like petrol
Although nothing was left,
Except rock and gathering ships
All glowing brightly.

Karl Brook (11)
Buckingham Primary School

WINTER

W   inter is here
I   cy water on the ground
N   ice soft snow all around
I   cicles twinkle on rooftops
E   very street is covered with snow
R   obins sing out loud and clear.

Ricky Braithwaite (10)
Chiltern Primary School

A SILENT WORLD

A silent world before your eyes
You're sure to find
The silent world
Is so still
Not as loud
As a morning in
Spring.

If you look outside
The window
You're sure to see
Roads are white
And children playing.

If you look outside
The door
You're sure to see
Birds in the trees
And snow on the ground.

Rachel Fee (10)
Chiltern Primary School

WINTER IS BACK

Winter is cold
It's really frosty
Snowmen are built
Icicles are out
Snowballs are flying around the street
Dogs are barking
Children are laughing.

Melanie Roberts (11)
Chiltern Primary School

WINTER

It's always chilly in wintertime,
Icicles hang above the door,
Snowflakes sparkle at night,
You sit alone in bed,
Shivering to death.
Your teeth are chattering,
The wind comes crashing on your window,
The frost sticks to your door,
The handle is too cold to touch,
The lock is getting rusty.
It's hard to turn the key,
The door
Does not want to open.

Katie Moody (10)
Chiltern Primary School

SNOW FALLING

I think of dangerous ice
In this silent world.
Kids throwing snowballs,
Swirling snowflakes
Falling to the ground.
The birds sing in the trees
There is a lovely breeze.
Kids building snowmen,
I see shivering people
Staring through windows
At all the warm fires.

Jamie Stainforth (10)
Chiltern Primary School

WINTER'S COME

Snow is falling,
Winter's come.
Children playing,
Laughter all around.
The snow falls white and gentle,
Falling softly.
Friends go carol singing,
I wish I could go.
Ice over lakes,
Can't go fishing!
Snow over hills,
Sledges hurtle down the hill.
Old people cold,
Horrible kids throwing snowballs at windows,
All the leaves off the trees.

Christine Griffin (11)
Chiltern Primary School

WINTER

Winter makes
your teeth chatter.
When it's icy
it looks sparkly.
When it snows
you can make
snowballs and snowmen.
All people shivering.

Sara Wiltshire (9)
Chiltern Primary School

IN THE SNOW

I was in the house
Looking out of the window
Nice white snow
I saw children pulling sledges
Laughing as they go.

People slipping on the ice
As they go to work
Children building snowmen
Robins singing in the trees.

'I can't go out in the snow' my mum said
'I will catch a cold'
My dad is on night shift
So he is warm in bed.

Cara Fox (9)
Chiltern Primary School

A WINTER'S DAY AND NIGHT

Winter has come
It's cold
Snowflakes are falling
And it sparkles.
Crispy leaves
People are coming in from the cold
Getting near the fire
Trying to get warm.

Kimberley Price (9)
Chiltern Primary School

IN WINTERTIME

There's always frozen ground
In wintertime.
People throw snowballs at each other,
We slip on dangerous ice.
Icicles are sharp,
People are cold
In wintertime.
The ground is frozen
In wintertime.
Always walk carefully
In wintertime.
You can't feel your feet
Under the snow
In wintertime.
You wear warm clothes
In wintertime.
Your arms are cold
In wintertime.
No one hardly opens the door
In wintertime.
You're always cold
In wintertime.
Dogs and cats
Are kept in the warmth
In wintertime.

David Blake (9)
Chiltern Primary School

WINTER WEATHER

The snow comes flying
as thick as it can be.
All over, the wind is whistling
louder and louder.
Icicles shaking, falling into
snow drifts.
Snow thickens whiter and whiter
lazily and incessantly floating
down and down.
Everything covered in a blanket
of ice.
The snow comes down silently
and stealthily, falling, falling
on the city brown.
Then the snow melts away
to come back another day.

Carl Sonley (10)
Chiltern Primary School

WINTER IS HERE

Winter is here,
With fluffy white snow,
With snowball fights,
People make snowmen,
Windows are frozen,
There is ice everywhere,
A silent night,
With a nice warm bed,
Winter is here.

Leah Calderwood (9)
Chiltern Primary School

THE COLD DAYS OF WINTER

The days of winter are cold and dead,
They are freezing,
The trees are bare and slippery,
Ice is hard like rocks,
You punch it,
You end up with a sore fist.

Snowmen are built, happy and delighted,
Melt when the early sun appears on the horizon,
Snow melts, winter is gone,
Come again soon.

Liam Rust (11)
Chiltern Primary School

CHILLY WINTER

One chilly winter's day
In the garden children play
Building snowmen, having fun
Out comes the cold, wintry sun.

Snowflakes fall to the ground
Throwing snowballs all around
Making slides for us to skid
It's really fun to be a kid.

Matthew Gallagher (9)
Chiltern Primary School

FROM THE BEDROOM

From the bedroom
I saw snow settling on the ground,
I saw the flakes spinning around.
It was a beautiful sight,
They were turning around.

Simon Ireland (9)
Chiltern Primary School

SNOWFLAKE

Snowflake,
shivery, soft,
silent, sharp, spotless,
goodbye beautiful snowflake
bye, snowflake.

Cheryl Christensen (9)
Chiltern Primary School

ICE

Ice,
chilly, cold,
icy, clear, shiny,
good to skate on,
ice.

Victoria Williams (9)
Chiltern Primary School

THE SEASIDE

Boats on the choppy sea tossed high in the air
The waves were crashing loud and high.
It was starting to snow
It was very bad
It kept biting my face
I had to put my gloves on
Because it was really cold on the beach.
All the boats and speedboats went by on the sea
The seagulls came to the beach
And there were hundreds of them
Huddled up tight to keep very warm.

Nicholas Dunhill (9)
Chiltern Primary School

UNTITLED

One snowy day it was icy
Children were playing in the snow.
Sledges went down hills and up hills
People were cold, falling over on the ice.
Icicles were hanging from houses
It was getting darker.
The snow stopped!
The ice melted!
The wind knocked trees down.
Strong wind
People were flying all over and falling down.

Sarah Windley (11)
Chiltern Primary School

THE WHITE SNOW

The white snow looks,
milky,
mighty,
it's magical,
mystical.

Christopher Lyon (8)
Chiltern Primary School

ICE

Ice,
chilly, frosty,
silent, slippery, icy,
must wear a hat,
ice.

Patrick Bywood (8)
Chiltern Primary School

SNOW

Snow,
soft, sparkly,
icy, freezing, sweet,
glittering in the night,
snow.

Samantha Sheppard (9)
Chiltern Primary School

MY GINGER BISCUIT

My ginger biscuit tastes,
spicy,
scrumptious,
it's smashing,
soft.

Joshua Hood (9)
Chiltern Primary School

THE KITTEN

The kitten looks,
cute,
cuddly,
it's cheerful,
clever.

Alex Gallagher (9)
Chiltern Primary School

THE ZOO

The zoo looks,
exotic,
enchanting,
it's exciting,
excellent.

Joshua Mills (8)
Chiltern Primary School

WINTER DAYS ARE HERE!

In the lakes I see no fish,
The branches of the trees lightly swish,
The snow is falling,
Wolves are calling,
Snowflakes are drifting,
Leaves are lifting,
On the fields are blankets of snow,
Fingers and faces start to glow,
Snowflakes floating really high,
Dark and dull grey in the sky,
Birds are singing,
Church bells are ringing.

Ross McCoid (10)
Chiltern Primary School

WINTER IS NO MORE!

In winter, in the morning sun,
Children jump out of bed,
Laughing, singing, shouting,
Looking forward to the day ahead
And when at last their mothers say,
'Breakfast's done go out to play,'
Running across the white, white fields,
Snow covering the trees with shields,
Making angels in the snow,
But signs of spring begin to show,
Winter is no more!

Ella Wood (10)
Chiltern Primary School

WINTERTIME IS HERE

White is all over in the town,
Snow is falling, falling down.

It's covering the doors and windowpanes,
Children are out playing their snowy games.

In the sky are clouds with a silver lining,
Snowflakes glistening, floating and flying.

Snow is in my hair,
Snow is everywhere.

Then in the night,
Everything is so white.

Animals start to sleep,
Close their eyes and occasionally peep.

Leah Beauchamp (9)
Chiltern Primary School

WHITE WINTER

Winter comes once a year,
All the children shout and cheer,
Wintertime is here.

Children's footprints in the snow,
Have a little silver glow.

On the rooftops the snow is soft
And it is cold in the loft.

Snowflakes twirl round and round,
Then they fall to the ground.

Alicia McKinney-Anderson (11)
Chiltern Primary School

SNOWDROPS

Snowdrops freeze
The city is cold with a shivering breeze
Snow, milk bottle white
Falls deeper in the dark night.
Shiny, silvery, white, fall the snowflakes
Children ice-skating on frozen lakes
Can hardly see through the thick mist
It covers the branches as big as my wrist.
Sheltering himself is the robin redbreast
From the wind blowing harder
From the distant west.
Now wintertime is ending and we say goodbye
While birds are singing high in the sky.

Debbie Mawer (9)
Chiltern Primary School

WINTER WORLD

The snow is perpetually falling,
Softly and silently drifting,
Falling, falling ever so softly,
Lakes are like mirrors,
Glistening like gems,
Turn your head and see,
The fields full of tiny little footprints,
Then there is the snowman glowing in the light,
As big as a bear giving you a fright.

Danielle Welsh (11)
Chiltern Primary School

THE WIND

The wind blows
while all quiet things are asleep.
All the animals are hibernating.

All you can hear
is the gentle whisper of the wind
and the distant sound of church bells.

The treetops sigh
while they are blown about.
The milk bottle snow crunches
under feet of children.

More snow clouds are forming in the sky
but the wind has fallen.
The sun is rising and the birds begin
to wake and sing.

Katie Tordoff (9)
Chiltern Primary School

WINTER FUN

Winter is the coldest time of year,
Icicles are cold and clear.
Garden ponds are hard with ice,
Lots of children think snow is nice.

Children like throwing snowballs,
At next door's garden wall.
Snow angel shapes are on the ground,
Across the road there's a snow mound.

Sarah Brown (10)
Chiltern Primary School

THE TIMES OF WINTER

When winter is near,
When the weather grows cold,
When the lakes ice over
And the leaves grow old,

The children are sledging in the snow,
Where parents are not keen to go,
They dress you up to keep you warm
Then you go playing at the break of dawn.

The treetops glisten, all sparkly white,
They sparkle and glisten all through the night,
The children are hoping for a cold, clear day
But the parents wish the snow would go away.

Larrissa Wolton (10)
Chiltern Primary School

WHAT I CAN HEAR IN WINTER

Wind blows the golden, crisp grass,
Music whispers in my ear
Like an instrument made with brass.
What is it I can hear?
I can hear birds whistling
And I celebrate winter with a cheer.
The trees are bristling,
The hills are steep,
So I go home to get some sleep.

Dean Hobson-Campbell (10)
Chiltern Primary School

WALKING DOWN THE SNOWY ROAD

I come out into the snowed over street.
As I approach the path I fall over
You can't imagine how cold it is!
It is like fields of snow.
As the snow comes flying at me
All I can think about is home
The destination I want to make.
There is only one me out there
The trees are coming at me
I admit I am scared.
There is no soft green grass
What I loved in summer
Just white everywhere.
Suddenly I see home
I walk into my house
Cuddling up to a blazing fire
But I will never forget that night.

James Lowe (11)
Chiltern Primary School

WINTERTIME

Snow is falling, settling over the houses
Like a big white blanket
The ground is frozen
Icicles hanging from high buildings
My nose is running
The ponds are iced over
Snowmen built in the far distance
Footprints in the snow
People sledging down steep, white, sparkly snow.

Rikki Harrison (10)
Chiltern Primary School

ME

Watching Mum doing the wallpapering,
I think that is very boring.

Watching Dad sitting in the chair,
I think he is not being fair.

I think Mum is working very hard,
All Alex does is play in the yard.

Watching Kailey watching TV,
All she does is yell at me!
'Be quiet Kelsie, shut up I'm watching TV!'

Watching Sheba playing with her ball,
All my mum does is yell and call.

Kelsie Carter (10)
Clifton Primary School

THE SEASIDE

At the seaside the sea is blue
And there are lots and lots of things to do,
Like build sandcastles and buy ice-creams,
Go in amusements and go on machines.

Now it's time to go
From the waves that flow
Back to my boring home I shall go.

Adam Douglas (9)
Clifton Primary School

RED

When I'm in love
I see red,
When I'm angry
I see red.

When I see poppies
I think of red,
When I see strawberries
I think of red,
When I see danger
I think of red,
When I see big flames
I think of red.

Put out the fire,
Now the red is dead.

Hayley Munro (10)
Clifton Primary School

I WISH I WAS A MONKEY!

I wish I was a monkey
Swinging in the trees
I'd never have to touch the floor
I'd swing about with ease.

I wish I was a monkey
I'd be so free
But when I come to think of it
No! I'm glad that I'm me!

Chelsea Sparrow (10)
Clifton Primary School

CHRISTMAS

As Christmas Eve is drawing near,
Santa Claus gears up his deer.
Prancer, Dancer, Rudolph too,
The toys are sealed with a blob of glue.
I emptied out my money box
And paid a trip to the corner shops,
To buy a present for Mum and Dad,
With all the pennies I once had.
For my brother I've knitted a bear,
With sewn on eyes and woolly hair.
TLC was top of my list,
Although this is something
I've never missed.
A Game boy if there's money to spare
And maybe a sparkly grip for my hair.
For the less fortunate, the weak and the sick,
All I can say is Santa please be quick!

Zoe Craddock (11)
Clifton Primary School

THE MONSTER

There is a monster with one big eye,
He stuffed his face in apple pie.
He was big and tall
And hairy and scary.
Then a witch cast a spell
And he turned into a fairy.

Callum Turner (9)
Clifton Primary School

DIGBY THE DOG

Digby the dog, got dirty digging,
A hole to hide his delicious bone in,
But then he said 'By God I've got it,
I'll put it in the fridge to keep it cool instead,
Then I'll go to bed.'

Kelly Barton (11)
Clifton Primary School

SEALS

S   eals are slippery and they
E   at fish
A   nd they swim in the sea
L   et's go and see them
S   o I wish that could be.

Natalie Evans (8)
Clifton Primary School

ABOUT SCHOOL

School is for listening,
School is for whispering,
School is for reading,
School is for writing,
That's what school is for.

Rachel Hargreaves (8)
Clifton Primary School

MY FAMILY

My mam wants a vacation,
My dad's glued to the PlayStation.
My brother Paul is on my Game Boy
So my mam says he is like a boy with a new toy.
My brother David's music is like a screeching lark,
So I am out the door and off to the park.
My cat Rags is in the summer sun, baking like a bun
But right now I think I will stay in the park
Because my family are *crazy!*

Sonya Morgan (11)
Clifton Primary School

THE DOME THAT GREW

I drew a picture of the Dome,
but in the morning it had grown.
It must have been sixty foot tall,
but it was still hanging on the wall.
I went inside, just to see,
just how much fun it could be.
The acrobats were hanging from the ceiling
and all of a sudden I had a funny feeling.
My mum didn't know I was at the Dome,
so I decided to go home.

Helen Abbott (10)
Cowick Primary School

I NEED MORE TIME

The lighthouse stands tall and proud upon the cliffs,
I can smell the sea and hear the gulls that ride upon the waves,
The stony beach stretches for miles,
I want to walk those miles,
There's just so much I want to do but haven't got the time.
The fields of lavender, purple, white and blue,
Gently wave their heads and let me smell their perfume,
There's crafts of every kind, glass and pottery too,
Antiques are everywhere and are always very fine.
The stately homes and the old windmills are on my list of finds,
I'll even pay the queen a visit like I did last time.
There's just so much I want to do but haven't got the time.

Katrina Barker (11)
Cowick Primary School

DAN

There once was a man named Dan,
Who lived in a rusty old van,
The poor old dude,
Had no food,
Therefore he ran to Japan.

Matthew Carey (10)
Cowick Primary School

MR MANKY PUTTS

Mr Manky Putts,
Was a real greedy guts.
He ate whenever able,
But once over fed,
He dropped down dead
And fell beneath the table.
His life came to a sudden halt,
For he had eaten too much salt.
At his funeral no one cried,
Even though they tried.
For it would no longer be harder,
To keep a full larder,
With Mr Manky Putts,
The real greedy guts,
As dead as a door nail,
Rotting slower than a snail.

But Mr Manky's wife,
Lived a full and exciting life.
Bungee jumping to abseiling
And then post mailing.
She would try almost anything,
Even flying off a building,
Jumping off the Eiffel Tower,
At 400 miles per hour.
She ended up in hospital quite a few times,
Where as an actress she learnt her lines.
Her body ended up bruised and battered,
Her hair fell out all tattered.
Now she's in a retirement home,
Right next to a mental safety zone!

Amie Louise Henderson (11)
Cowick Primary School

AN INVITATION

It's my birthday tomorrow,
Do you want to come?
You'd better bring a present,
Or I'll tell my mum.

We'll have frogs' legs and snails,
Maggot stew too.
How about blood, it tastes real good.
You can have butter from the gutter
And that looks like lead.

We'll watch videos all night,
Hope they don't give you a fright.
They're aged eighteen,
But if your mum doesn't agree,
Then you won't stay for tea.

We'll play some games,
How about musical chairs,
But if I don't win,
You'll be locked under the stairs.
We'll then have a dance contest,
I bet I am the best.

So if you want to come,
Be especially nice,
But I don't really think,
You'll win the prize!

Geraldine Buckley (11)
Cowick Primary School

A SHRINKING POTION

Throw in the heart of a pig,
The bark of a twig,
Lung of a bat,
Tail of a cat,
You're getting it,
But that's just the first bit.

Drop in the stomach of a dog,
The intestines of a frog,
Leg of an ant,
Eye of an elephant,
You've nearly done it,
Now for the last bit.

Chuck in smelly school custard,
Mould of rotten mustard,
Maggoty cakes,
Sour milkshakes,
That's it, excellent,
A shrinking potion,
You're very intelligent.

Chloe Waterson (11)
Cowick Primary School

A WINTER'S BREEZE

On a cold winter's day,
When the snow is sparkling white,
A gentle breeze blows by.
All is silent except for that winter breeze,
Roaring like a tiger, but as harmless as a kitten.
The many noble spirits of the past
Are flowing with the breeze,
Searching for their loved ones.
A robin sits and stares into the wind,
Like me
Then it takes flight
And soars free.
How I wish I could go with him and fly
Anywhere I wanted.
I sit outside and watch the winter sunset,
A beautiful sight.
The many colours merge, until the sun disappears.
I sit until the stars come out,
Then I walk home and try to get to sleep,
Listening to the winter breeze.

Willis Hall (11)
Cowick Primary School

THE PHOENIX

Fiery feathery bird
Lives forever and flies
Iridescent bird
Fantasy creature
Like a fiery furnace
Charmed atmosphere around him.

Shaun Bexley (11)
Estcourt Primary School

THE WITCH

Black clothes, pointed hat
All dark as midnight
Eyes staring at gruesome tongues,
Ears pointed,
Hearing every sound and move,
Scaly, pimpled chin
Like a dagger waiting to stab,
Lips; thin blue and skinny
Never been touched by lipstick.
Nose, pimpled on each side
With hair as black as midnight,
Sniffing everywhere she goes.
Overgrown toe nails
Waiting for a scrub,
Bring out a smell which can kill us
Chanting her dismal spell round a cauldron.

Cooking, cleaning, washing clothes,
Bright skirts and belly tops.
All skin smooth and peach
Pimples gone
Had a bath,
Smells of roses in green grass.
Spotless house
Not a spider in sight.

Leigh Tomlinson (11)
Estcourt Primary School

KENNING - DOG

Cat-catcher,
Door-scratcher,
Angry-growler,
Night-howler,
Meat-eater,
Warm-heater,
Hole-digger,
Mine's-bigger,
Wet-noses,
Picture-poses,
Good-swimmer,
Coats-glimmer.

Scott Walsh (10)
Estcourt Primary School

A KENNING

Cage climber;
Night-timer;
Cage fighter;
Day sleeper;
Quiet creeper;
Ball runner;
A real stunner;
A tiny creature;
Few features.

Louis Suddaby (9)
Estcourt Primary School

KENNING

Fish-eater
Fierce-creature
Flesh-ripper
Bone-gripper
Blood-drinker
Boat-sinker
Rough-gills
Always-kills
Eats-feet
And-meat
On the run
Weighs a ton.

Gareth Jones (10)
Estcourt Primary School

A KENNING

Wing-flapper
Head-tapper
Seed-eater
Ball-beater
Perch-sitter
Seed-litterer
Coat-ripper
Finger-nipper
Air-soaring
Loud-tweet
Hates-meat.

Robert Anderson (11)
Estcourt Primary School

THE MINOTAUR

Sharp piercing horns like spears
Hair like spikes of wood
Muscles bulging, mighty like steel
Threatening bristling teeth
Worn-away hooves like carved stones
Stamps like a herd of elephants

A fear of dark caves
Only eats fruit
Helps grannies across the street
And tries not to step on people
With his feet

Robert Shiels (11)
Estcourt Primary School

KENNING

Flesh-stripper
Bad-nipper
Fish-eater
Man-eater
Rough-gills
Always-kills
Fast-swimmer
Water-skimmer
Good-sight
Bad-fright
Fierce-creature
No-teacher.

Samuel McDonald (10)
Estcourt Primary School

FRANKENSTEIN

A bolted neck,
Holding a dark, massive, green head,
That looks like a trash can.
He has fingers like pencils,
He never takes a bath,
He was brought to life by a thunderbolt,
His body is the size of a school desk,
His legs are like snake skin,
Dry and scaly.

But he has got a secret,
He is scared of the dark,
He always keeps his light on
And a torch just in case
But if the light goes out,
He'll hide under his pillow.

Christopher Mansfield (10)
Estcourt Primary School

THE WEREWOLF

Gruesome fangs,
As long as your fingers,
Big, bulging eyes,
as wide as a golf ball.
Massive claws like knives
Waiting to tear you apart.
A smell of reeking, deceased people,
Laying in his den.
Saliva dripping from his mouth
Like a fountain, pouring on the floor.
He waits in his den for some prey.

Andrew Isle (11)
Estcourt Primary School

THE MERMAID

Her multicoloured hair
Glistening in the sea.
The smooth, silky skin of her face,
Sparkling in the sun,
Her everlasting help
Saves fishes' lives
Her tiny beady, sea blue eyes
Microscopic nose
So smooth that fish will slide straight down it.
Lips so shiny
Looking like a dazzling star in the sky,
The scaly brilliant clothes,
Brightened by the sun,
The sound of her voice
Singing like the wind.
Bubbles drifting across the water
Bursting on the surface.

Laura Waslin (10)
Estcourt Primary School

THE CREATURE

Howling, ferocious creature
Moves like lightning
Towards the victim
Pounces on you with its spiky claws
Its fangs tearing your flesh apart
Sometimes it's invisible
You do not know it's there
Creeping behind you
Ready to rip you apart.

But after he jumps on his victim
He does not feel like eating
He would rather get his sharp teeth
Into some juicy vegetable
He would dig up a 100 gardens
Just to get his claws
Into a delicious dripping tomato
Just for a little bit more taste
He drinks champagne.

Matthew Parker (11)
Estcourt Primary School

THE SCARED WEREWOLF

The vile, hairy, disgusting beast
Plundered down the dark alleyway,
Looking for its next big feast.
Determined not to run away,
As it walked down the dingy street,
He caught a glimpse of something sweet.
A ferocious and violent beast,
A transformed creature.
It is a nocturnal beast,
It has sharp teeth like daggers.
The beast is a carnivore,
It is hairy, has sharp claws like razor sharp knives.
It transforms on a full moon
A howling beast.
It is a destructive and brutal beast.

Michael Anderson (10)
Estcourt Primary School

THE MINOTAUR

The Minotaur's mean, with human-like hair
It storms around its home like the beast it is
With a pig nose and sharp horns
Waits for its prey to pull it apart with its muscly body
The meanest thing in ancient Greece
Only it knows the way out of its muddling
Spaghetti-like maze.

His wife comes in
Who is very small
Drives that Minotaur up the wall
She's muscly but very thin
The poor man's head ends up in the bin
To his wife he acts like a mouse
He creeps and crawls round the house
When his wife goes out he is very happy
Just like Scooby Doo's nephew Scrappy.

Scott Sharlotte (9)
Estcourt Primary School

THE DEVIL

Fire monster, person
Waiting patiently in Hell
A destructive, departed, lifeless person,
Living in a bottomless pit of the Earth.
Outrageous, petrifying monster
With sharp piercing horns.
He moves with the speed of light,
Jagged claws like knives piercing your flesh
Leaving you dripping with blood.

This substantial monster
He hates fire,
But loves water.
He is a swot at school.
This vicious monster gets bullied
This beastly disagreeable horrid monster,
Has turned in to a pleasant, kind, friendly person.

Ricky F Sheriff (11)
Estcourt Primary School

THE GOBLIN

A naughty, noisy natured creature
With a crazy and short tempered mind.
He has had no discipline
And magic is his game,
A tiny bad mannered creature
With glaring green eyes
And a pointed nose like a sharp stick,
A large mouth with small pointed teeth.
He is stubborn and careless
With a wrinkly complexion like a crumpled up piece of paper
He has long bony fingers
And is hairy and rough.
He stamps as he walks
Wearing his pointed hat.

When he's out and about,
He helps everyone
To carry shopping or paint a shed.
He always says please and thank you too,
Instead of being mean,
He's kind just like you.

Danielle Cooper (9)
Estcourt Primary School

THE FAIRY

The exquisite, tiny fairy
With her enchanting, dazzling wings
Is an elegant, tiny human form
Her dainty feet twinkle
As she flies across the skies
The tiny dress she wears
Glittering in the darkness
Her big blue eyes as bright as the sky
Her glorious blonde hair
As yellow as a daffodil
The glittering dress she wears
Fades away as she flies off
Into the darkness
At home she is obnoxious
Puts horrible spells on people
At school she destroys
All of the toys
She blames other people
Bonks them on the head
Screws up paper
Shouts at the teacher
And kicks people black and blue.

Grace Nicholson (10)
Estcourt Primary School

THE SKELETON

He is bony, skinless and unwise.
clang, bang, clattering with his bony body.
No eyeballs, lip less, no skin no nothing
Just his deafening noisy bones,
Clanging when he walks
He is not colourful
But he is dazzling white
Moving like he is dancing in a ball,
Coming out of a grave
Putting his bones back together noisily
He lives in a damp squalid home,
He sleeps in a coffin
Can you hear the rattling?
He is trying to escape.

At night instead of being stubborn,
He smiles merrily
And then he opens his coffin,
Slowly and quietly!
He runs down the street
'Hello' he said
'Would you like a sweet?'
But all the other people scattered like fire,
'Wait, wait, wait!' he said
And stumbles back to bed.

Ashlea Claffey (10)
Estcourt Primary School

THE GIANT

The huge, one-eyed monster
Awaits for its prey,
In the dingy dark, haunted cave,
No light at all.
It's a carnivore creature,
With excellent hearing
But I'd beware,
As it becomes night, he comes out.
When morning comes, people
Are missing from their beds
And the monster, for the rest of the day
Is locked in his cave.

Nikki Parker (10)
Estcourt Primary School

THE GIANTESS

An immeasurable, bulky, enormous creature.
With a head as big as a bedroom
And like a ghost, transparent.
Her hair is like a lion's mane,
Legs as hairy as a orang-utan,
Ears like balloons, just level with her eyes.
The feel of her body, jagged, bristling
Oh so rough.
Earth trembles as she walks down the street.

Stacie Reffin (10)
Estcourt Primary School

THE JUDGE

Circle of rotten horns on his head
Bald, pale, blue, sickly.
Deadly to the bone he touches
Face like a piece of scrunched up paper.
Fangs that drip saliva.
A deep, dull voice that gives you a headache.
Eyes glow red after he has killed.
Sent by the Devil
To get rid of humans.
Invincible killing machine.

He tried to make friends
But that silly old Judge
Shook their hands
And they turned to dust.
He cried and cried
'Till his eyes turned sore
He wasn't seen anymore.
Not 'til a hundred years later
And then he struck again
To make friends and end all pain.

Sarah Ockelton (11)
Estcourt Primary School

STEAM TRAIN

Through the back,
Across the track,
Into the station,
Across the nation,
Like a team,
It lets out steam.

Ashley Bland (10)
Hornsea Community Primary School

FOOTBALL

Roar goes the crowd,
As the ball enters the net.
A dog ran onto the pitch,
so we took him to the vet.

Four minutes to go,
We had to hold tight.
Two players were arguing
But then it became a fight.

The ref blew his whistle
Gave him the card - red
So the player walked off
And went home to bed.

James Bowman (11)
Hornsea Community Primary School

SNAKES

Snake slithering across the floor
Ready to attack with its fangs.
Rattling its tongue like maracas
Eating its prey in one.

The scaly, scales camouflaged
No-one can see him,
Until he attacks in a flash
He squeezes until the death.

Andrew Walker (11)
Hornsea Community Primary School

FIREWORKS

The fireworks whizz
The fireworks fizz
The fireworks blow
The fireworks glow
All through the night
The fireworks crash
The fireworks flash
The fireworks bash
The fireworks clash
All through the night
The fireworks burn
The fireworks turn
The fireworks flare
The fireworks glare
All through the night.

Callum Thompson (10)
Hornsea Community Primary School

THE CANAL BOAT

The canal boat turns the corner,
'Full steam ahead,' shouts the driver.
The engine starts to cough and splutter,
Then the captain spins the rudder,
This way and that,
The canal boat swerves,
Up! Down!
And gone forever.

Richard Oates (10)
Hornsea Community Primary School

The Tiger

We are known as the tigers,
The mightiest of them all,
We stroll across the jungles,
And over plains from dusk to fall,
We watch over our newborn cubs,
And teach them all we know,
We show them the way to survive,
And sit back and watch them grow,
For the tiger is one of the strongest,
A tiger is one to respect,
The tiger is a wild cat,
And the cutest, we expect.

Hannah McNeil (10)
Hornsea Community Primary School

The Monster

There's a monster under the stairs
He wears a pair of flares
He eats our shoes
He eats our coats
Whatever we put under the stairs
He has three fingers and three toes
Six eyes and one red nose
His horns are yellow his teeth are green
He's the ugliest thing I've ever seen.

Aaron Dawick (11)
Hornsea Community Primary School

PEACE

Wouldn't peace be wonderful,
If everything was calm,
And everyone could get along,
No one do any harm.

If we think back to World War Two,
We see people fighting for world peace.
That also happened in World War One,
It took four years to cease.

Hunting needs to be stopped,
There are endangered species galore.
Please stop it all right now,
I can't take it anymore!

Now if we all work together,
Peace could be brought back.
Yes, wouldn't peace be wonderful,
Nastiness could get the sack.

Freyja Fitzpatrick-Hilditch (10)
Hornsea Community Primary School

SANDS

Hailstones like gravel
Grinding on a window
Snow like crumbling biscuits
Leaves like a squirrel,
Running through the trees
Sea like scraping sandpaper
Crashing on the wall.

Anneiga Drage (10)
Hornsea Community Primary School

READING

When I read a book at night, that I haven't already read,
The letters seem to come alive and my imagination spreads.
I see colours and written words, shoot around my room,
And pirates hanging off cliffs, before they fall to their doom.

I like to read factual books, to hear about funny things.
I like to read bird books, to hear about their giant wings.
I like to read lots of books, different in every way,
People think I read too much, but believe me, I'm OK.

Books are really, kind of my life,
I think I'll need them more than a wife.
Books are the best thing that happened to me,
With words that last forever like the big blue sea.

But don't think I just like books,
I also like making, just like cooks.
Mixing up a really tasty recipe,
I like to write, don't you see.

I also like to draw doodles,
With yummy stuff like spaghetti noodles,
So my imagination can run free,
Come and have a look and you'll see.

I love books, with that I agree,
But there are things more important to me,
Like family, friends and exercise,
Those are the things that make you come alive.

David Simpson (11)
Hornsea Community Primary School

THE DERBY

I trudge into the Stadium of Light,
Take my seat, read the programme
and hope there's not a fight.
between the Mackems and the Mags!
The Tyne 'n Wear derby is tonight!

The referee seems to be black 'n white.
There's already some confrontation!
The security guards try to stop the fight.
While they score! They cheer! They dance! They prance!
We groan and moan. We might score and that's a big might!

2-0 down with Phillips on the run!
It's a goal! Gloom lifts! Rejoice fills the stands!
Jumping up and down it sounds like a tank explosion! *Fun!*
2-1 down we've got a better chance in the second half.
The lottery's coming up with cash to be won.

2-1 down we could equalise and make it 2-2!
Second half we're all enthusiastic!
Meanwhile my sister's eating a yoghurt called Froo-Froo.
Sunderland score we all feel fantastic!
Yes! We made it 2-2!

After the match we all celebrate!
The first derby ever in that stadium.
After, we all walk around in debate,
If Phillips was offside?
Who cares, because when I get home, I feel all tingly inside!

Bruce Ridley (11)
Hornsea Community Primary School

ARTILLERY

Long range guns mounted on wheels,
Artillery,
Upon the hill with target in sight
Cannons, guns mounted ready to fire,
Mortars,
Boom! A large explosion arises from the ground.
Grenades,
The explosion fills the clouds pink with anger,
Bombs
The smell of cordite, drifts through the trees,
Bazookas,
Guns recoil sleek and black,
Machine guns,
Long range guns mounted on wheels,
Artillery.

Mark Embleton (11)
Hornsea Community Primary School

MY FAVOURITE SOUNDS

The rumbling of the classic bikes, starting a race.
The roaring of the crowd, standing up when the ball goes in the net.
The blasting of a rocket, going into outer space.
The sizzling sound of bacon frying in a pan.
The screaming of the crowd, as the band appears on stage.
The sound as Meatloaf starts their song on the electric guitars.

Kieran J McBeth (10)
Hornsea Community Primary School

SPIDERS

You'll find me in your bath,
Most people are scared of me,
But I'm more scared of them than they are of me.

I have to be quick because they chase me round the house,
Running and screaming like I'm a lion,
But I'm not a lion, I'm a small spider.
I won't hurt you,
I only want to be your friend.

I just want to say 'Hello.'
I hide in my lonely cold web crying,
All I want is to be your friend,
But every time I say 'Hello,' you run and scream and scare me.

I have no friends, I'm all alone, hungry and scared,
I curl up at night with no one to talk to.
My only friend is myself.

So next time you see me, remember, I only want to be your friend,
So please don't run and scream,
I won't hurt you so please don't hurt me.

Victoria Bishop (11)
Hornsea Community Primary School

SNOW

Trees whistling in the wood
Snow falling on the ground
Birds talking in the trees
Peace is all around.

Lisa Lambert (10)
Hornsea Community Primary School

THE ICE MAN

His eyes as bright as fire
His nails as sharp as knives
His hands as cold as a freezer
His clothes as blue as the sea.

He sneaks into the night,
When everyone's asleep
He freezes all the houses,
And never gets a rest,
Until the dawn begins to break.

When everyone wakes up
And the children go to school.
They see all the ice,
And begin to slide and slip
One of them falls and hurts himself.
It's the Ice Man's fault!

Hannah Lawson (11)
Hornsea Community Primary School

DOLPHINS

Dolphins
Adorable little creatures,
In danger of man
Swimming beautifully through the water.

Diving under for fish,
But in danger from sharks
Getting caught in fishing nets
There colours are as blue as the sky.

Karen Symonds-Tate (11)
Hornsea Community Primary School

MY FUNKY FRIENDS

Lively Lucy likes her juicy
Raving Ruth lost her tooth
Groovy Grace won the race
Barmy Becky broke her necky
Charming Chloe loves Mr Snowy
Luscious Lorna sits in the sauna
Happy Hannah makes a banana
Smiling Sam eats roast ham
Kicking Katy is my matey
Lovely Lisa likes pineapple pizza
Kiwi Kirsty gets very thirsty
Smelly Sophie is a bit dopey
Disco Danielle has a cocker Spaniel
Cheeky Chelle has a friend called Mel.

Rachel Rhodes (11)
Hornsea Community Primary School

BOOKS

Picture books, story books, fiction and non-fiction books,
Spooky books, boring books, hide behind the sofa books,
Pop group books, fantasy books, Jacqueline Wilson too.
Dictionaries, thesauruses all the spelling books.
Bibles and folk tale books have been passed down through the family.
Old books, new books, modern and old fashioned books,
Enid Blyton, Joyce Stranger, write some good books too.
So you see some good books and some bad as well
But books aren't so bad,
You wouldn't be reading this poem if they were.

Amanda Smith (11)
Hornsea Community Primary School

MY STRANGE MATES

Lucy Lemon loves her lemonade.
Rhubarb Ruth grew a tooth.
Rachel Raspberry bought a blackberry.
Sophie Strawberry is always dawdling.
Funky Freyja is a football player.
Danni Diver is a scuba diver.
Vicious Vicky is very tricky.
Nagging Natalie is always patting me.
Loopy Louise eats lots of cheese.
Lovely Lorna loves the saunas.
Cuddly Chloe goes absolutely barmy.
Charming Chelsea has gone a bit crazy.
Groovy Grace loves to race.

Becky Rhodes (11)
Hornsea Community Primary School

KESTREL

Up, up and away,
I soar through the sky,
Looking for my prey,
What do I spy.

I spy,
A little mouse, scurrying for its life,
From me of course, I spied it there,
Running for its life.

There's more to me
Than you can see,
I hover and I swoop
Right through the day sky.

But at night,
I go to sleep
Anywhere I can,
My friend the owl then comes out,
To see if the night has come.

Pip Dove (11)
Hornsea Community Primary School

STREAMS

Draping over the steps of stones,
Tickling the base of its fall,
The water will scrape along,
Bubbles of foam will gather in bits
And silently drip, drop off in the distance.

It can whoosh past at a violent pace,
But it lightly sways and shiffle and shuffle,
From miles away you hear it dripping,
The silent stream goes on forever.

Wispy waves tumble down,
Through the crack of the stream and peep through
To the sheet of water hanging down.

Kirsty Clegg (11)
Hornsea Community Primary School

RALLY ON THE OUTBACK

Start,
Tyres, compound, drills buzzing.
Engines roar, times fuzzing.
Sponsors, paintwork, people part.
The line up is all ready to start.
Five, four, three, two, one . . .
There goes the starting gun.

Up, off, away they go.
Cars, keep up with the flow.
Subaru, Ford, Peugeot too.
There stands a wall, they all go through.
Battered paintwork, twisted metal.
Car parts, dust clouds settle.
After that they still keep going.
An ashy track, times flowing.

Halfway through.
Three cars out.
Tyres blow, stewards count.
'Left 90 over crest.'
Peugeot 206 is doing the best.
'Oh no' we're deceived.
Vauxhall Astra 1st place received.

Intermediate three and still the Astra.
It turned in too tight, and disaster!
Peugeot passing the mangled car,
And just about three seconds afar.
Up a straight, filled with bumps,
Round a corner and then a jump . . .
Up, over, down, *Crash!*
Five metres, four, three, two, one. 125mph *finish!*

Jack Billam (11)
Hornsea Community Primary School

CARS!

Touring cars, F1, cars galore,
There is so much, much more.

Audis, Volvos and BMWs too,
They'll all do for me and for you.

Ladas are cheap but they will fall apart,
If you are unlucky, you will find one that's got the heart.

Ferraris are fast and so are McLarens,
But behind are the police in slow Volkswagens

Mercs are luxurious and Lexus are too,
But most common are Vauxhalls and they're fine for me and you.

Jonathan Worsdale (10)
Hornsea Community Primary School

THE GREAT JUNGLE

The roaring jungle
The raging animals
And the trees that shade
The animals such as
The leopard shelter under a tree.
To stop the bright sun making him boiling hot.
The cheetah runs in the baking sun
Trying to capture its prey.
The galloping antelope
Running away from lions and pumas.
The parrot squawks at other birds and insects.
The lizard scurries across the steaming hot land.
Trying to get to the water.
This must be a fantastic life for the animals.

Samantha Watson (10)
Kellington Primary School

THE DROWNING JUNGLE

Monsoon madness -
Torrential rain,
Chokes the jungle.

Lizards lurk,
Trying to dodge,
The heavy rain -
They succeed.

Tigers peep through,
The wet bushes -
Their yellow eyes
Like balls of fire.

Leaves shuffle by,
Hands in their pockets,
The river gargles,
With pride.

The lion snarls,
Trying to avoid the
Path of destruction,
That destroys the jungle.

Venus flytraps
Keeping their mouths shut,
Waiting for the rain,
To stop.

The black tongue,
Of the snake,
Lashes across
The winding river

Monsoon madness
Torrential rain
Chokes the jungle.

Laura Evans-Booth (10)
Kellington Primary School

FLYING HIGH

I can see the tiny people staring up at me
While I glide through the air
My neck twists and turns
From left to right
I see an artist
Twirl his stroking brush
To and fro
The strong sun
Forces its beams on my dehydrated feathers
I feel like an aeroplane
Being bombed by the German army
Struggling for somewhere to land
I feel a jab in my wing
It is a green, prickly bush
Now the big people dash towards me
Feeling claustrophobic
A pleasing man picks me up
And takes the razor sharp
Stick out of my wound
He gets it out and he sets me free!

Ellie Robinson (11)
Kellington Primary School

EAGLE

The tremendous creature dived
Out of the sky
Pouncing on a school of mice
As they scatter on the moonlit ground
Running for their little lives
Running so they don't get caught
And become a feast for the eagle
He swoops, he grabs two
One by the tail
And one by the stomach
One narrowly escapes pure death
And hides
The eagle devours his prey
Squeaks of pain come
As the eagle punctures the mouse
He drops the carcass
And glides to rest.

Daniel Baker (11)
Kellington Primary School

IT'S A JUNGLE OUT THERE

Monsoon madness -
Raging rain
Attacking the jungle.

Lime lizards scatter,
Away from the rain
The yellow eyes stare,
Like a statue
As it looks for any danger.

Tiger terror as it looks for prey
In terrifying conditions
Roaring tantrums of the mouth
As the razor sharp teeth,
Punctures an unknown creature.

Tim Addy (11)
Kellington Primary School

THE LEOPARD

The leopard pounces on its prey
The deer runs for its life
It was too late - it had been caught
The leopard took it home.

The cubs crowded round
Dug their teeth in and begun to eat
Their eyes were golden like fire
Could it be, will they be here tomorrow?

Then it will start again
The day goes the same
Do they have a life to live?
Off they go hunting.

They catch a deer
Take it home
And then they eat it.

Off to sleep they go.

Gemma Reeson (11)
Kellington Primary School

MONSTROUS MONSOON

Monsoon madness -
Ruthless rain,
Pounds the jungle.

Lost lizards struggle,
To escape perpetual peril,
They merely escape,
As the floods begin to rise.

The terrifying tiger,
Runs through bushes as big as elephants,
With eyes as bright as stars,
Trying to escape the merciless Lord.

The chasing cheetah,
Is now being chased,
Through its own territory,
By its own worst nightmare.

Tarantulas scurry to their nests,
To defend their frightened young,
Their webs hardly survive,
The long and painful torture.

The river bursts its bank,
Making a pathway of destruction,
Crocodiles crawl for cover,
Iguanas just ignore.

Monsoon madness -
Relentless rain,
Injures the jungle yet again!

Stephen Gudgeon (11)
Kellington Primary School

THE TIGER

The tiger
Creeps towards its prey
An unsuspecting deer
It pounces
It punctures its skin.

The deer
Dies slowly and painfully
The tiger sinks its teeth into the skin of the deer
And drags the prey to his deep and dingy lair
To feed his tigress and cubs.

The pack
Rips the skin off
Like it was butter
They devour the organs
Saving the heart for last.

The tiger
Drags the bones, without a speck of blood on them,
To the back of the lair
Nice and quiet
The cubs cuddle up into a ball to sleep.

The tigress
Goes out to hunt
Will she catch a deer
Will she catch a zebra
Or will the hunter be hunted?

Luke Bednall (11)
Kellington Primary School

IN THE JUNGLE

Hailstones hammer down
It returns again.

Lazy lizards stare
With their huge black eyes
Dark as night

The lively lions
Close their mouths
At night and open them
At day

The lime lizards leap
From tree to tree
Slipping and sliding about

The mischievous cheetah
Runs from the evil
Then everyone finds a shelter.

Amy Winter (9)
Kellington Primary School

GOLDFISH

They swim around in a bowl all day
They have silly names like Jaws.
They eat fish flakes,
Just like they were cakes.
They really are pretty boring,
After all they only have seven second memories,
And they don't do anything,
They don't even blink,
But they constantly drink.

Tim Russell (11)
St Mary's & St Joseph's RC Primary School

ALPHABET MANIA

A is for Adam
Who likes to go to the shops

B is for Bob
Who wants a lollipop

C is for Charlie
Who has a nice hat

D is for Derek
Who has a fast rat

E is for Edward
Who has a great band

F is for Fred
Who likes to play in the sand

G is for Greg
Who likes to go to the fair

H is for Helen
Who can't decide what to wear

I is for Isaac
Who likes to brush his hair

J is for Jonathan
Who does not like to share.

Rory Tipping (8)
St Mary's & St Joseph's RC Primary School

MY ALPHABET POEM

A is for Anne
Who is very fat

B is for Brian
Who has a cuddly cat

C is for Cedric
Who plays all day

D is for Daniel
Who doesn't do a thing his mum says

E is for Edward
Who eats all morning

F is for Fred
Who is always yawning

G is for George
Who is a good boy

H is for Helen
Who plays with her boys.

Jennifer Hughes (8)
St Mary's & St Joseph's RC Primary School

FOOTBALL MAD!

Football is the number one sport,
The FA cup is in my thoughts.
In Scotland, my uncle drinking gin,
Celtic is going to win, win, win.

This year England just got in
The Euro, but they will never win.
I think Sweden have a good chance
They will easily beat Holland and France.

Then the World Cup's two years away
And the Cup Final's along the way
Then the ball goes in the net
Then my friend ran after his pet.

Football is the number one sport,
All the cups are in my thoughts.

James Hepburn (10)
St Mary's & St Joseph's RC Primary School

MY ALPHABET POEM

A is for Ant
who marches all day

B is for bat
who cries in May

C is for cat
who is cuddly and sweet

D is for dog
who likes to eat meat

E is for elephant
who likes to shop

F is for fox
who has a ginger top

G is for guinea pig
who wears a wig

H is for hen
who likes to dig.

Heather Plimmer (9)
St Mary's & St Joseph's RC Primary School

THE MILLENNIUM

The millennium means 2000 years have passed away,
We are very lucky to see this day.
Parties are going on all night,
Fireworks make the sky look bright.
The Pope addressed the square in Rome,
The Queen was sat in the Millennium Dome
The Eiffel Tower set alight,
With fireworks this very special night.
In London in Trafalgar Square,
There have been lots of parties there.
I went to London on the 2nd of Jan,
There was rubbish around including cans.
Pop stars were singing all night long.
At midnight you could hear the church bells
Go ding dong.
But with all this excitement
Most of us forgot,
That the millennium was made,
For Jesus Christ son of God.

Jessica Forbester (9)
St Mary's & St Joseph's RC Primary School

MY POEM

You can throw me high
You can throw me low
You can kick me high into the sky
You can roll me gently on the ground
You can kick me low on the ground
What am I?

Ellie Holbrough (7)
St Mary's & St Joseph's RC Primary School

MY DREAM WORLD

In my dream world there would be:
World peace instead of war.
In my dream world there would be:
Rich folk and no people poor.
In my dream world there would be:
No such thing as bad.
In my dream world there would be:
No such thing as sad.
In my dream world there would be:
Food for everyone.
In my dream world there would be:
An everlasting sun.
In my dream world there would be:
Only one feeling . . . Glee!

Olivia Brown (8)
St Mary's & St Joseph's RC Primary School

FOOTBALL IN 2000

It's 2000 years since Christ was born
And in the 2000 years football was formed.

Over 2000 matches have been played and
Thousands of teams have been made.
I'm in two football teams of my own so I
Should know football was made a long time ago.

My favourite team of them all is Man U for
They score them all.
My favourite player is Ryan Giggs for he runs
Down the wing like a greyhound in a spin.

Edward Walker (11)
St Mary's & St Joseph's RC Primary School

FOOTBALL ALPHABET

A is for Arsenal
Who are not good at all

B is for Bradford
Who can't kick a ball

C is for Chelsea
Who are quite good

D is for Derby
Who get stuck in the mud

E is for Everton
Dressed in blue

F is for Fulham
Who need the loo!

Mitchell Scollen (8)
St Mary's & St Joseph's RC Primary School

MY KITTEN TIGGER

My kitten Tigger
She is so cute
Even my mum says she's a beaut
She has soft padded paws
With very sharp claws
She has a soft furry coat
Keep her warm on any boat
She tries to catch the fish
And eat them in her dish
She has a soft warm purr
I love her
My kitten Tigger.

Stacey Richardson (9)
St Mary's & St Joseph's RC Primary School

MY ALPHABET POEM

A is for Anne
Who has a cat.

B is for Betty
She always wears a hat.

C is for Claire
Who does not like to share.

D is for David
Who acts like a bear.

E is for Eric
Who is football mad.

F is for Fred
Who is very bad.

Claire Hancock (8)
St Mary's & St Joseph's RC Primary School

2000 THE MILLENNIUM

2000 fireworks light up the sky
2000 little eyes watch them fly.
Just think, 2000 years since Christ was born.
The Dome was lit with lights so bright.
The midnight sky as light as the sun
Lots of people celebrating with a bun.
People celebrating in different ways.
People watch the clock strike 12.
Lots of parties worldwide,
Some people counting down 10, 9, 8, 7, 6, 5, 4, 3, 2, 1 with pride.
Did you stay awake?
No neither did I.

Ben Forbester (9)
St Mary's & St Joseph's RC Primary School

MY ALPHABET POEM

A is for Anne,
Who is very fat.

B is for Brian,
Who has a cuddly cat.

C is for Cedric,
Who plays all day.

D is for Daniel,
Who doesn't do a thing his mum says!

E is for Eddy,
Who eats sweets all day.

F is for Fay,
Who watches Summer Bay.

H is for Helen,
Who never wants to play.

Emma Russell (7)
St Mary's & St Joseph's RC Primary School

HAPPINESS IS SADNESS

Happiness is when you get a new pet.
Happiness is when you go to bed.
Sadness is when you move.
Sadness is when your pet dies.
Happiness is when you find a new friend.
Happiness is when your mum is having a baby.
Sadness is when you break your leg.
Sadness is when people say nasty things.

Rebecca Cusack (7)
St Mary's & St Joseph's RC Primary School

MY ALPHABET POEM

A is for Anne
Who likes toast.

B is for Brad
Who likes me the most.

C is for Claire
Who likes to play.

D is for Deric
Who plays with his cat all day.

E is for Eric
Who likes to play with his toys.

F is for Fred
Who likes to make some noise.

Michael Richardson (8)
St Mary's & St Joseph's RC Primary School

MY BABY BROTHER

He's got two big brown eyes,
And a little button nose,
Twelve big white teeth,
And ten tiny toes,

He's cute, he's gorgeous, he's loveable too,
Because he's a boy we dress him in blue,
He gets up to mischief when Mum's back is turned,
So don't turn your back Mum, a lesson has been learnt,

He's my baby brother and his name is Sean,
And my happiest day, was the day he was born.

Angela Coffey (9)
St Mary's & St Joseph's RC Primary School

MY ALPHABET POEM

A is for Anne
Who is not nice.

B is for Ben
Who has got mice.

C is for Cath
Who likes cats.

D is for Daniel
Who has a lot of mats.

E is for Emily
Who likes dogs.

F is for Fred
Who likes frogs.

Shonagh Hepburn (7)
St Mary's & St Joseph's RC Primary School

DEAR MY VALENTINE . . .

I think you are wonderful,
I think you are cute,
You are so remarkable,
You're a real beaut,

You're my desire,
You're my treasure,
Your look makes me feel
As light as a feather.

You are so attractive,
And your looks are so fine,
Oh please,
Oh please,
Be my valentine . . .

Elizabeth-Anne Coffey (10)
St Mary's & St Joseph's RC Primary School

NEWCASTLE FOOTBALL CLUB

Shearer and Ferguson make a great team
So every time they play
They are the theme.

If you ever see Shearer not on the pitch
All the fans will be saying
Make a switch.

If you ever see a red card
Don't take it hard.

If you ever see an opposition's goal
Make their net have a hole.

If you see Solano score
Make the fans shout more, more, more.

The match was great, you must admit
Up until the ball came to Lee
And fell in a pit.

Joel Saltmer
St Mary's & St Joseph's RC Primary School

MY ALPHABET POEM

A is for Anne
Who is very clean.

B is for Bob
Who does not like to be seen.

C is for Claire
Who plays all day.

D is for Daniel
Who likes to play.

E is for Emily
Who is nice.

F is for Fred
Who likes mice.

Araminta Rowlatt (7)
St Mary's & St Joseph's RC Primary School

OUR SCHOOL TEAM

Our school team isn't particularly mean,
If we were more aggressive we would be
Much more possessive,
I think that our team rocks,
We're located in Pock.
We've got Alex Brown, who's down in defence,
And steady Eddy in midfield.
We've got Ben who likes to head,
But if you get in the way it might knock you dead.
The worst we've ever been beaten was 13-1,
The goals just went in one by one!

Philip Marshall (10)
St Mary's & St Joseph's RC Primary School

SCHOOL

School, school,
School is the best,
School is better than all the rest,
School contains education
Lots of work and multiplication,
School has literacy,
School has maths,
You should never miss your class,
Always be at school on time,
Or you could be put at the back of the line,
At lunch there is lots of food,
Never be naughty or the teachers will get in a mood,
Home time arrives,
We say our goodbyes.

Joanna Smith (9)
St Mary's & St Joseph's RC Primary School

THE FINAL

Did you see the final clash?
Camara gave Ince a bash,
Did you see Owen's goal?
After the shot the net had a hole!
Did you see the keepers catch?
It really was a great match,
Did you see Fowler's smack?
I think it bent the keepers hand back!
Did you see on the TV?
Did you feel the atmosphere?
Did you shout the people out?
Did you see it? Did you see it?
No neither did I!

Jonathan Cusack (10)
St Mary's & St Joseph's RC Primary School

THE HIPPO

The hippo plodded along
Humming himself a beautiful song.
The huge heavy hippo heaved himself about,
Showing stomach, feet and mouth
As pink as any trout.
Rolling in mud and playing in water,
Trying to copy his daughter.

His skin is scaly and rough,
And his rear is extremely tough.
The hunters are always after the horn,
So sometimes the hippo wishes he had never been born.

Going home when the day is done,
To sleep under the setting sun.

Lindsey Hoyle (10)
St Mary's & St Joseph's RC Primary School

THE DRAGON

Its fiery breath is the colour of the sun,
Its scaly body weighs a ton.

It's green, red, orange or yellow,
It's certainly not tame to any odd fellow.

Its wings are so fine,
You travel through time.

It travels day or night,
Prepared for any type of flight.

They live in caves by the sea,
They shoot fire at the enemy.

Charlotte Linsley (10)
St Mary's & St Joseph's RC Primary School

ANIMALS

Some are small,
Some are tall,
Some don't even exist at all.
Some are skinny,
Some are fat
Like an overgrown rat.
Some have legs,
Some have tails
Some are even bigger than whales.
Some crawl,
Some walk,
Only parrots talk.
Animals have feelings too,
So they liked to be loved by you.

Leanne Vere (11)
St Mary's & St Joseph's RC Primary School

MY SISTER

My big sister is very mean,
But that's quite normal cos she's a teen.
She wears lots of make-up on her face,
And her bedroom is a very messy place.
There's lots of chewing gum wrappers on the floor,
But when I pick them up she always drops more.

But then again she can be kind,
When there is something on my mind.
She teaches me all her dances,
And tells me all about her romances.
She's very witty and really pretty,
And after all I love her!

Jinny Hardy (10)
St Mary's & St Joseph's RC Primary School

ALPHABALL

A is for Arsenal
Who are fat

B is for Bradford
Who plays like Postman Pat

C is for Chelsea
Who are good

D is for Doncaster
Who are a real mate

E is for Everton
Who are all dressed in blue

F is for Fulham
Who always need the loo!

G is for Glasgow
Who are always rude

H is for Hearts
Who are always in a mood

I is for Ipswich
Who aren't the best team in the land

J is for St Johnstone
Who are football banned.

Kieran Anderson (9)
St Mary's & St Joseph's RC Primary School

FAR AWAY IN A TROPICAL LAND

Far away in a tropical land
Seas are swaying up and down
People dancing on the sand
In a tropical land!

Every bright light comes from the sky
Sun or moon or each little star
Hear a baby dolphin cry
In a tropical land!

Fishes swimming in the seas
Swaying, swishing up and down
Sitting in a pineapple tree
In a tropical land!

In the shade of this paradise
On the beaches late at night
Eating lots of lovely rice
In a tropical land!

People fishing in a boat
Waves are jumping round and round
Catch a fish with a pretty coat
In a tropical land!

Far away in a tropical land
Seas are swaying up and down
People dancing on the sand
In a tropical land!

Gabrielle Jones (9)
St Mary's & St Joseph's RC Primary School

MY CAPPYBAARA

My cappybaara
A real star-a
Totally brilliant rodent
They are the size of dogs,
And they look like hogs,
And can often be haunted down.

The live in herds,
And can be hunted by birds,
But they always put up a fight.

They walk about when it is light,
But their relatives - hamsters
Stay up at night.

Cappybaaras are scared,
They make a squeaky sound.
They're squidgy and podgy,
And fast and round.

Cappybaaras have adapted,
Very well to their wild.
'They can reach 3'5"
When they are a child.

Alexander Brown (11)
St Mary's & St Joseph's RC Primary School

MONDAY'S CHILD

Monday's child is really grim
Tuesday's child drinks a lot of gin
Wednesday's child is really weird
Thursday's child is growing a beard
Friday's child winds me up a lot
Saturday's child has a spot
And the one that's born on the seventh day
is snotty, grotty and very spotty.

James Meadowcroft (9)
St Vincent's RC Primary School

THAT MAN FROM BOMBAY

There was an old man from Bombay
Who thought it was sunny one day
Then it began to rain
And he fell down a drain
That silly old man from Bombay.

Natasha Todd (9)
St Vincent's RC Primary School

SPACE

S   hooting stars everywhere
P   lanets that are red here and there
A   liens in their UFOs
C   rafty things with a big, long nose
E   ven scarier when you smell their toes.

Christopher Dixon (9)
St Vincent's RC Primary School

MISCHIEVOUS MICHAEL

Mischievous Michael, he is bad,
He makes his nanny very sad,
If he's in trouble he'll make you chase
And then he'll punch you in the face.
Mischievous Michael always says no,
Especially when it's time to go,
To bed, for he hates this,
If you make him, he will hiss.
To hit people he just loves
And don't go near him, for he shoves.
In this poem, I've made it clear,
If you see him, don't go near.

Jack Burnham (9)
St Vincent's RC Primary School

THE DRAGON

The dragon slept upon his bed.
His claws were sharp, his eyes were red.
He takes to eating people whole
and never stops to use a bowl.
And, until a knight discovered this,
the poor dragon slept in peace.
The knight said 'Let's kill this mangy beast,
before it has us for a feast.'
Of which the dragon produced,
some army tanks, to break the ranks.
The knights broke rank and fled,
Leaving the dragon home in bed.

Jack Oyston (10)
St Vincent's RC Primary School

WHEN I WENT TO THE SEASIDE

One day when I went to the beach
There was so much I could see.
I stripped off straight away (with my cossie underneath)
And jumped into the sea!
While I was in,
A crab crept by
It nipped my toe
And so I started to cry.
I ran to my mummy,
Who thought it was funny.

After all the events of the day,
I think that I'll have to say,
My toe doesn't hurt any more!

Annie Wykes (9)
St Vincent's RC Primary School

OUTER SPACE

Silence is when you're alone in space
Planets all around the human race.
Aliens lurk in our solar system
Come visiting us on planet Earth
Extra terrestrials could be your neighbour.

An alien's UFO car
Goes faster than a shooting star
It dodges planets every day
Going faster in the month of May.

Ross Walker (9)
St Vincent's RC Primary School

SCHOOL DINNERS

Going outside,
Playing in the yard,
Dinner ladies saying get inside,
The kids are playing very hard.

Food fight, food fight,
Mash everywhere,
Peas in you face,
What a disgrace.

Going in for dinner,
Standing in the line,
Get a plate
Dinner ladies shoving food on the plate.

Food fight, food fight,
Mash everywhere,
Peas in your face,
What a disgrace.

Charlotte Stather (9)
St Vincent's RC Primary School

SCHOOL DINNERS

Hairs again, hairs again, they're always in my food.
I pray to God that soon the caterers will be sued.
Yucky, mucky mash, they plonked on my plate.
The smell of roast potatoes, I think I'm going to faint.
We always have the same old stuff.
I think that's gone far enough.

Lauren Lambert (10)
St Vincent's RC Primary School

LAUGHABLE LIMERICKS

There was an old man from China,
Who sharpened his nails even finer,
He cut them away,
They re-grew the next day
And he lives on a bottle of cider.

There was a young man from New York,
Who lives on a diet of pork,
He ate so much meat,
He grew enormous feet
And built his house on a fork.

There was an old lady from Mars,
Who ate in a day, ten cars,
She was stabbed by a knife,
Came back to life,
In prison she ate all the bars.

Andrew Murray (10)
St Vincent's RC Primary School

MY BEDTIME

Tucked in bed, all nice and tight
Please make sure the bed bugs won't bite,
Creepy crawlies on the stairs,
Hairy monsters come in pairs,
I shout to my mum
To tell her to come
But she cannot hear me
I have to get up to do a wee
What will happen to me, I wonder.

Natalie Hinchsliff (10)
St Vincent's RC Primary School

LAUGHTER IN THE AIR

There was an old woman from the stars,
Who had a million cars,
She was so rich,
She married a man called Mitch,
That silly, old woman from the stars.

There was an old man from France,
Who did an unusual dance,
He was so funny,
He smacked his mummy,
That silly old man from France.

Callum Sweeting (9)
St Vincent's RC Primary School

MASH POTATO

Mash potato is horrid
It rumbles in my tummy.
When my baby sister eats it
It sticks all over her dummy.

White and fluffy, like cotton wool
All white, not bright, but dull.

Mash potato with gravy
Well that's a different matter
It's gorgeous
Even though it could make you fatter.

Louis Ramsay (10)
St Vincent's RC Primary School

WHAT WAS THAT?

In the distance, bells chime at midnight,
Branches scrape against the window, giving me a fright.
Round the room pairs of eyes stare down on me,
So under the covers I will flee.

Creeping round like a mouse,
Creeping round the empty house.
On the dimly lit landing,
I imagine a dark figure standing.
The headless doll that was once so small,
Now has a huge shadow upon the wall.

I couldn't sleep for the rain
And the wind rattling the windowpane.
Lightning lit up the spooky staircase
My heart pounding as if it was in a race.

There was a deadly silence,
I peeped out my covers,
I stared at my door, the key turned
Slowly and dropped to the floor.

What was it last night,
That came when there was no light?

Lizzy Butler (10)
St Vincent's RC Primary School

DARK

Thump, thump, thump,
Rising up my stair.
Thump, thump, thump
Driving me insane.

Banging on the bathroom door,
Like a deadly drum.
Who's there? Who's there?

Am I dreaming, hurry, hurry,
Wake me please, from this
Mad nightmare.

I think I'm sweating,
Like a pig
Even trembling, like a
Huge earthquake has hit.

Thump, thump, thump,
Coming along the landing.
Thump, thump, thump,
Driving me insane.

Opening my bedroom door
Who's there? Who's there?

The glass in my window,
I'm sure is going to crack.
I can feel its presence
Cold, evil and scary.

I'm shouting, wailing, howling,
But no one can hear my cries.

Thump, thump, thump,
Wriggling around my bed.
Thump, thump, thump,
Who's there? Who's there?

Lizzy Currie (11)
St Vincent's RC Primary School

FEAR OF THE DARK

I awoke . . .
There was a rustle from the trees,
They were saying to me
Danger, danger, danger.

I could tell by the way they swayed
From side to side
Tapped at the window
The wind blew through their leaves . . .

It was dark and damp,
Shadows chased me around my room . . .

Then suddenly thump, thump, thump,
A noise from downstairs,
I sneakily crept down, I saw nothing.

Silently settling in my bed
I fall asleep listening to the noises
Thump, bump, thump.

Jacinta Insole (10)
St Vincent's RC Primary School

THE NIGHT

I woke up sharply,
Hearing wild, pattering on the windows
What should I do?
Smelling the incense my dad has
Rushing out of bed to see the time.
I hear a sharp movement
Is this a dream? I scream inside my head.
The cold now getting to me
Running down the stairs
Was that a person?
Deep, mysterious shadows swaying softly, creep up on me.
My heart pumping,
I slam the door, it seems to echo,
Feeling trapped I run back to my room.
Before I could get there
Click, click,
Lights turn on,
My family stood at their bedroom doors
Oh no!

Etta Hawksworth (10)
St Vincent's RC Primary School

EARTH

The Earth is like a giant Smartie
But instead of being flat, it's round
There's chocolate on the inside
And crispy shell all round.

The houses are made of gingerbread
There's everything you can eat
But don't eat too much or else
You'll never get out of your seat.

What if your mum wasn't there?
You can eat as much as you want
So go on and eat, eat, eat,
The goodies are really sweet.

The middle of the Earth is melted chocolate
With a burning fire underneath
There's candy biscuits everywhere
And a strawberry wreath.

Jacinta Hickson (10)
St Vincent's RC Primary School

DARK

I sat up astonished,
Sweat running down my head,
My mouth dry with fear,
The shadow in my room
Leaning over my bed,
Began to draw near,
More sweat down my head.
The wind blowing against my window
Will it ever stop?
Shaking the panel,
Trembling from head to toe,
Imagining the worst,
I got under my covers,
The silence was deadly,
Like an unused graveyard,
Afraid and alone,
Got to be brave,
Do I want to know?
Whose shadow is on my wall?
Do I want to know?

Molly Mangan (11)
St Vincent's RC Primary School

WHAT WAS THAT?

What could it be?
The creaking of the stairs, are those eyes looking at me?
Who could it be?
The scratching and thumping,
The whispers of voices
Something's out there waiting for me
Is that a ghost shining on the wall?
The brown teddy once so small
And all of a sudden so very tall.
Shadows moving around the room,
My heart pounding like a drum, boom, boom.
Shivers down my spine
Goosebumps on my arms and legs.
The hairs on my neck sticking up on end,
Fusty smells all around my room.
What's that noise going bang, bang, boom?
I know it, I know it, there's something out there waiting for me!

Eleanor Leach (10)
St Vincent's RC Primary School

FEAR OF THE NIGHT . . .

Trees scraping against my window sill,
There I lay in bed, so still,
My heart pounding like a drum,
Shivering from head to toe, sucking my thumb.

Sweating, like raindrops on my face,
Hearing a stranger on my staircase,
Getting louder, here he comes,
While creaking of the radiator quietly hums.

Staring at the door, the outline's on my floor,
Snuggle down my sheets,
The movement of feet,
I sense the fear, he or she was coming near.

I got out of my bed,
Shaking my head,
I opened the door,
There on the floor was my baby sister.

Holly Caprani (11)
St Vincent's RC Primary School

FEAR OF THE NIGHT

I woke up, why?
Trees rattling against the window.
Movements downstairs,
Creaking of doors.
Don't be silly, there won't be anything, will there?
My heart throbbing,
I was sweaty and sticky.

Shadows moving outside my bedroom door,
Moonlight pouring into my bedroom window.
What did wake me? I don't know.
My heart is still throbbing,
Shaking like mad, shivering won't stop.
Door's opening, about to scream,
Nothing came out.
Gran, it was you, oh gosh what a fright,
What a fright, goodnight!

Emily Watson (10)
St Vincent's RC Primary School

FEAR OF THE DARK

I woke up at the noise of the torrential rain,
The whistling of the wind starts my fear,
I leapt under the bed sheets, there's no going back,
Wondering whether my courage has gone.

Something tapping on the windowpane,
There's something hooting in the roof,
I know it, I know it,
There's goosebumps on my goosebumps,
There's sweat on my head
And shadows zoom by on my wall.

The floor has started creaking,
'Who is there?' I try to say,
But the words would not come out,
But stayed in my mind,
My fear's getting stronger,
My door has opened slightly with a creak, creak, *creak!*

I hold my breath, close my eyes tight,
Feeling the beat of my heart in my head,
Hoping that it's all gone away,
But it hasn't.

Ben Dawson (11)
St Vincent's RC Primary School

SCARED OF THE DARK!

What woke me from my sleep?
Could it have been the tapping on the window?
Huh, what is that shadow behind the curtain?
Was it just my imagination?
My heart is pounding like a drum,
What's that tapping under the bed?

Who's turning the handle?
The wind is howling like a dog,
Who's creeping up the stairs?
What's that light outside?
Oh, it's just Dad with his torch,
Ah, who's that calling my name?
Silly me, it's just Mum and Dad.

Nathan Caprani (11)
St Vincent's RC Primary School

WHAT WAS THAT?

As I lay there in my bed
Horrible things going round my head.
The wind and rain clattering against the window,
Cats miaowing, dogs barking, owls hooting,
The smell of the damp hall
Wafting around the house.
Went downstairs and found
A shadow moving around.
What could it be?
Who could it be?
Could it be my imagination tricking me?
Could it be a burglar stealing my courage?
Or a dog jumping and bouncing,
A young child running riot,
What could it be?
I crept back upstairs, all I heard
Was creak, creak, creak.
My heart was pounding
Like a child jumping on a trampoline.
My hair's sticking up on end,
Goosebumps all over my body.

Hannah Loader (10)
St Vincent's RC Primary School

FEAR OF THE DARK

Creak, creak, creak, creak go the stairs,
Bang, bang, bang, bang goes the loft.
Is there something in my room
Or maybe in the loft?
It was pitch-black, I couldn't see a thing,
There's a long, black shadow sliding along the walls,
What could it be or is it nothing?
There's sweat dripping off my head.
My heart was racing like a car
I couldn't sleep in bed.
Crash! what was that?
Was it someone coming or something falling?
I didn't know a thing.

Joe Mellors (11)
St Vincent's RC Primary School

FEAR OF THE DARK

I was in a dark, gloomy hall
I could see a big, black, fierce dog
With big, green eyes
Trying to stare me out.
An arrow passed me
I ducked with a scream
It stuck into a book with a 'clang'.
I saw a shadow
Going into a room
He shut the door with a 'bang'.
I could hear a floorboard creaking
As I walked into the hall
With total silence.

Jack Williamson (10)
St Vincent's RC Primary School

FEAR OF THE DARK

I can hear the wind howling,
I hide under my bed,
My heart's pounding like mad,
Thump, thump, thump,
The windows are clattering,
There's voices outside my door,
Who can it be?
I opened the door,
The chair swinging back and forth.
I can smell homemade cooking
What can it be?
I shut my window
I can't hear anything,
It was only the wind
What a relief!

Mike Naama (10)
St Vincent's RC Primary School

ROADS

Red, orange, green brightly flashing
Hundreds of cars honking and dashing.
Cars wanting to get by
Pollution makes you die.
Cars crashing just like bangs
That is the horrible motoring gangs.
Robbers all over the place
They might steal your video case.
Honks that wake you from your sleep
It'll even make your alarm go 'beep'.

Mark Richardson (8)
St Vincent's RC Primary School

FEAR OF THE DARK

What was that I thought?
I could feel my heart pounding,
I could feel the sweat running down my head,
Suddenly I heard the floorboards creak,
I got out of bed and looked at the time, it was midnight,
I opened the door and ran downstairs,
In the darkness my mind started to play tricks on me,
It was driving me mad,
I stopped, I could hear tapping on the window, what could it be?
Was it the trees, was it a cat or was it the wind?
I saw a crooked shadow,
I ran as fast as I could back to my bedroom
and jumped under my covers.

Max Brown (10)
St Vincent's RC Primary School

FEAR OF THE . . . DARK

As I lie asleep in my bed
Nasty things rush through my mind
Someone's coming up my stairs
My heart is pounding like a drum.

Thump, thump, crash!
What do you want? I gasped with fear
But there was no reply except the voice getting closer.

The moonlight shone through my dark, ghostly room
I could smell the sweat running down my face
'Who is it?' I kept asking myself.

Sarah Marsden (11)
St Vincent's RC Primary School

THE DARK

I don't like the dark creeping over my head,
I don't like the dark swirling all round my bed,
I don't like the dark creeping over my head.

It feels like a chimpanzee,
Looming right over me,
It feels like a chimpanzee.

When Tony turns out the light,
Everything goes out of sight,
When Tony turns out the light.

But all of the books are closed tight,
Now it's time for goodnight,
Yes, all the books are closed tight.

Antony Good (9)
St Vincent's RC Primary School

FEAR OF THE . . . DARK

As I lie in my bed
All of a sudden there's a noise
I run to the window to see
What's the matter . . .

I see a shivering, shining, shaking shadow
Coming up the stairs
I smell burning from the kitchen
I hear the keys rattle from the door
What was coming up the stairs?
Was it the man with the silver knife?
Or was it just my mum?
I probably did not see anything, or did I?

Lucy Stephens (10)
St Vincent's RC Primary School

SHARK

'Shark
Who, who are you?'
'Who?
            I'm shark, swimmer of swimmers
            Beware of the great white.'

'Who, who are you?'
'Who?
            I'm shark, king of all sharks
            Proud of my fin.'

'Who, who are you?'
'Who?
            I'm shark, dangerous and hungry,
            Proud of my sharp teeth.'

'Who, who are you?'
'Who?
            I'm shark, I live in the sea,
            Beware!'

Thomas Watson (8)
St Vincent's RC Primary School

HATING THE DARK

I don't like the dark, spinning round in my room,
It feels like the house is full of gloom,
I don't like the dark, spinning round in my room.

I don't like the dark, looking down on me,
It feels like there's someone I just can't see,
I don't like the dark, looking down on me.

I don't like the dark, climbing onto my bed,
I get so frightened, I cuddle my ted,
I don't like the dark, climbing onto my bed.

But I don't like the dark, swirling round my toys,
Though it doesn't make any noise,
Yes, I don't like the dark, swirling round my toys,
When it's dark and quiet, it really annoys.

Katherine Gregory (8)
St Vincent's RC Primary School

ELEPHANT

'Elephant who, who are you?'
'Who?
          I am elephant
          Biggest animal in the world
          I have big, chunky legs.'

'Who, who are you?'
'Who?
          I am elephant
          Proud of my trunk
          I make loud noises
          I squirt water from my trunk.'

'Who, who are you?'
'Who?
          I am elephant
          I have a tail like a rope
          I have tusks like spiky branches.'

Joshua Burley (8)
St Vincent's RC Primary School

THE DARK

I don't like the dark, coming into my bed,
It feels like it's going to grab my head,
I don't like the dark, coming into my bed.

I wish my dad had left the light,
It feels like something might just start a fight,
I wish my dad had left the light.

I hate the dark in my eyes,
It makes me feel that I'm about to cry,
I hate the dark in my eyes.

But in my mum's bed, it's safe and sound,
You can't see anything, not even the ground,
Yes, in my mum's bed, it's safe and sound,
So I'll stay till morning is found.

George Mangan (9)
St Vincent's RC Primary School

AT THE ZOO

Hungry animals at the zoo,
Some old and some new.
In the playground children screaming,
In the cages the caretaker cleaning.
A tarantula in a burrow hiding,
While the nasty snake is sliding.
At the eagle people are staring,
At the people, the eagle is glaring.
The speaker announces 'Time to go
I hope you all enjoyed the show'.

Alexander Wood (9)
St Vincent's RC Primary School

NEXT DOOR

Next door's music blaring out,
My mum begins to shout.
The dog starts to bark,
While it's getting very dark.
Every week of the year,
They're out drinking beer.
Counting sheep,
Trying to sleep.
Mum went round to their door,
I can't stand it any more.
It sounded like a zoo,
What was going on? I haven't a clue.

Paul Naama (9)
St Vincent's RC Primary School

A RIDDLE

I live in a cage,
I don't earn a wage,
I eat lots and lots of nuts,
I go tuts, tuts, tuts.
Sometimes I run around,
My feet do not pound,
I tumble on my little wheel,
If you hold me I will squeal.
What am I?
(I am a hamster)

Naomi Watson (8)
St Vincent's RC Primary School

TIGER

'Tiger
Who, who are you?'
'Who?

> I am tiger
> Live in the African plains
> Fierce and very hungry
> Stripy like a bee.'

'Who, who are you?'
'Who?

> I am tiger
> King of cats
> Proud of my speed
> Hunting for my prey.'

'Who, who are you?'
'Who?

> I am tiger
> Runner of runners
> Crouching in the daylight
> Be very afraid
> Beware!'

Abbie Walton (8)
St Vincent's RC Primary School

NO LOVE FOR ME

The bell rings, the blossom blooms,
The sound of birds singing is beautiful.
I wish I had love.

The sun is shining, the flowers are fabulous,
Men and women are holding hands.
I wish I had love.

People dancing and jumping around,
Rabbits hopping together and eating with each other.
I wish I had love.

Everyone is strolling around,
The world is colourful and happy.
I wish I was colourful inside.
I wish I had love.

Joseph Gateshill (8)
St Vincent's RC Primary School

TIGER

'Tiger
Who, who are you?'
'Who?
            I am tiger
            Cruel and sneaky
            Jumper of jumpers.'

'Who, who are you?'
'Who?
            I am tiger
            Big and angry
            A good sense of smell
            King of the African plains.'

'Who, who are you?'
'Who?
            I am tiger
            Fat and clever
            Proud of my sharp claws and teeth
            Sly and fierce
            Beware!'

Corin France (9)
St Vincent's RC Primary School

LION

'Lion
Who, who are you?'
'Who?

    I am lion
    Runner of runners
    King of cats.'

'Who, who are you?'
'Who?

    I am lion
    Proud of my mane
    Night eyes understanding
    Fierce and hungry.'

'Who, who are you?'
'Who?

    I am lion
    Prowling in the night beams
    Hunting animals
    Fierce beyond imagination
    Sharp teeth
    Beware.'

Suzanne Deyes (9)
St Vincent's RC Primary School

THE DARK

I don't like the dark when it fills up my room,
It makes me feel scared and full of doom,
I don't like the dark when it fills up my room.

I don't like the dark surrounding my bed,
It makes me think scary things in my head,
I don't like the dark surrounding my bed.

I don't like the dark, there might be something I can't see,
Like a monster walking up to my bed going to grab me,
I don't like the dark, there might be something I can't see.

But in my bed it's nice and secure,
You can't see the light or the door,
Yes, in my bed it's nice and secure,
You can't see the window or the door.

Sophie Kavallares Simpson (9)
St Vincent's RC Primary School

SQUIRREL

'Who, who are you?'
'Who?

      I am squirrel
      Running up trees
      A marvellous sight, my bushy tail.'

'Who, who are you?'
'Who?

      I am squirrel
      Watch out at night
      And you might see me.'

'Who, who are you?'
'Who?

      I am squirrel
      Eating nuts
      Never bite people
      Hibernate in winter
      Be quiet!'

Samantha Vizor (9)
St Vincent's RC Primary School

RATTLESNAKE OF THE DESERT PLAINS

'Rattlesnake
Who, who are you?'
'Who?
       I am rattlesnake
       Skin shedder
       King of the desert plains.'

'Who, who are you?'
'Who?
       I am rattlesnake
       Tongue for a nose
       Slither of slitherers.'

'Who, who are you?'
'Who?
       I am rattlesnake
       Hiding in the grass
       Warning rattle sound.'

'Who, who are you?'
'Who?
       I am rattlesnake
       Armless and legless
       Hunter for mice
       Smooth like paper
       Deadly sting
       Beware!'

Reuben Seetal (9)
St Vincent's RC Primary School

THE PLAYGROUND

Bouncing feet make a pounding noise,
Playing football, it's the boys.
Lots of loud, jumping feet,
Football players feel the heat.
All the fans are really happy,
The other team are very snappy.
Very loudly the whistle blows,
The gang of losers blow their nose.

Daniel Haigh (9)
St Vincent's RC Primary School

SWIMMING POOL

In the swimming pool running about,
Most of the pupils start to shout.
Lots of people making bubbles,
It takes away all your troubles.
The lifeguard is whistling,
Nobody is listening.
It's time to get out,
Now nobody is about.

Amy Dakin (8)
St Vincent's RC Primary School

IN THE PLAYGROUND

Sad children screaming
Happy ones are beaming.
In the noisy playground
Falling children can be found.
People fighting and being mean,
The teacher on duty has been seen.
Noisy children go to the headmaster,
A little girl is crying, she needs a plaster.

Stephanie Thompson (9)
St Vincent's RC Primary School

A RIDDLE

I live in a tree
I like to be free.
I have a red, bushy tail,
But I don't fail.
I have a little, brown nose,
I sneak a drink from a hose.
I'm hairy and brown,
I don't wear a gown.
(I am a squirrel)

Melissa O'Connell (9)
St Vincent's RC Primary School

DOLPHIN OF THE OCEAN

'Dolphin
Who, who are you?'
'Who?
          I am dolphin
          Flipping in the sunbeams
          Friendly beyond comprehension.'

'Who, who are you?'
'Who?
          I am dolphin
          Swimming in the sunset
          Diving through the ocean
          Clever beyond imagination.'

'Who, who are you?'
'Who?
          I am dolphin
          Jumping through the sunlight
          Diver of divers
          Friendly to humans.'

Caroline Fish (9)
St Vincent's RC Primary School

IN THE TV ROOM

The TV is on full blast,
Sophie's always home last.
Hannah shouts at Lizzy,
Mum's always busy.
The cat sits purring like mad,
James is in bed really bad.
Dad is sleeping, he is dreaming,
Lizzy's crying like a baby and she is screaming.

James Butler (8)
St Vincent's RC Primary School

ALLIGATOR

'Alligator
Who?
Who are you?
Who?'

        'I am Alligator
        Proud of my sharp teeth
        Fast in the river
        Slow on the ground.'

'Who?
Who are you?
Who?

        'I am Alligator
        Cruel and hungry
        Leader of rivers
        Sneaking in the sunlight.'

'Who?
Who are you?
Who?'

        'I am Alligator
        Fierce beyond imagination
        Thick skin
        Love my prey
        Beware.'

David Smith (9)
St Vincent's RC Primary School

FRUSTRATION

Frustration is red and yellow,
It smells like rotten cheese on stale bread,
It tastes like steamy sausages,
Sounds like chalk scraping down the board,
Feels like soapy cornflakes,
It lives in your *temper!*

Natasha Dennison (10)
Stockwell Primary School

ELEGY TO A SMARTIE

There it sat
It looked like a football
Crunched like a rock in my mouth.
Tasted like silk
I felt glum
Bye bye Smartie
Farewell.

John Carr (10)
Stockwell Primary School

HAPPINESS

Happiness is multicoloured,
It smells like melted chocolate.
Happiness tastes like Neapolitan ice-cream,
It sounds like angels singing,
It feels like soft sheep's wool.
Happiness lives in the heart of a rainbow.

Emma Chapman (9)
Stockwell Primary School

MEMORIES OF MY NANNA

I remember her as if she was still alive,
By the way she brushed my hair and her kind voice,
The bad memories I also remember, the way she slept
And the pain is the worst thing I remember about her.
To see her take her medication made me break down,
But worst of all I heard that she died of cancer in the early hours.
That hurts me the most.

Sophie Johnson (9)
Stockwell Primary School

MEMORIES OF MY GREAT GRANDMA

I remember my great grandma's snowy white hair.
She always gave me a pound when I went to see her.
I remember her stories about the war,
But she was always ready for a laugh and a joke.
I remember pushing her in her wheelchair,
Old and frail but still could laugh out loud.
She was ninety-three years old when she died of old age.

Chelsea Dent (9)
Stockwell Primary School

MEMORIES OF MY CAT

I remember my cat,
She was very active.
Her name was Jerry,
She used to play with my teddies.
She ran out of the gate,
And she got knocked down by a car.
I will always remember her because she
Woke me up in the middle of the night.
We always used to have races and my mum
Always says, 'Don't cry, she will be living happily in heaven.'
I always think about her and cry just thinking about her death.

Melanie Roberts (10)
Stockwell Primary School

FEAR

Fear is icy blue,
Smells like poisonous gasses,
Tastes like sour lemons,
Sounds like crackling fireworks,
Feels like a painful disease,
Lives in a grey dungeon.

Shane Gorbutt (9)
Stockwell Primary School

ELEGY TO A SMARTIE

There it sat
Round like a football
Brown as mud
Crunched like a crab.
Taste so chocolatey
Felt so soft
But now I'm sad
Because it's gone.
Farewell Smartie.

Jade Priestman (9)
Stockwell Primary School

PAIN!

The colour of pain is bright red,
It smells like burning iron,
It tastes like chilli spice,
It sounds like spitting liver,
It feels like a spark, like a pointed blade in you,
It lives in flames of fire.

Natalie Clarke (9)
Stockwell Primary School

FEAR POEM

Fear is icy blue,
Smells like revolting gasses
Like the oil down below.
Tastes like sour lemons
Which I do not like one bit.
Sounds like crackling fireworks
Whizzing through the night sky.
Feels like pain trying to break
Your heart into a thousand pieces.
Lives in a dungeon dark and smelly.

John Esders (10)
Stockwell Primary School

ANGER

Anger is crimson.
Anger smells like burnt fire.
Anger tastes like burnt rotten cheese.
Anger sounds like fireworks banging.
Anger feels like hot sharp glass.
Anger lives in your heart.

Gregg Blanchard (10)
Stockwell Primary School

ELEGY TO A SMARTIE

There it sat,
Looking like a button
As green as grass
Cracking like a fire
I feel sad and glum
It's gone forever.

Kay Taylor (10)
Stockwell Primary School

ANGER

Anger is like a sunset,
It smells like the smoke of a fire,
It tastes like burning bangers,
Sounds like a blasting radio,
Feels like a charging mad bull,
And it lives in the heart of volcanoes.

Thomas Dervey (9)
Stockwell Primary School

FEAR

The colour of fear is black,
It smells like a pink pig's back.
It tastes like a big black tyre,
And it sounds like bubbling fire.
It feels like a hard black ball,
It lives in a dark market stall.

Emma Louise Bones (10)
Stockwell Primary School

HOPE

Hope is as white as snow,
It smells like roses and dandelions,
It tastes like sweet cherries,
It sounds like a little robin singing,
It feels like soft, smooth silk,
It lives on a wonderful forest.

Wendy Whisker (10)
Stockwell Primary School

JOY

Joy is like a sky so blue,
It smells like sugar and spice.
Joy tastes like a cream bun,
It sounds like quiet, sweet music.
Joy feels like clean water,
It lives in lovely Heaven itself.

Daniel Green (10)
Stockwell Primary School

BEAUTY!

Beauty is pink and yellow,
It smells like fresh baked bread.
Beauty tastes like a white marshmallow,
It sounds like a cat purring in bed.
Beauty feels like a rabbit's soft white fur,
It lives in the bottom of a big brown bear.

Chloe Arnold (10)
Stockwell Primary School

SEASIDE LIFE

Dawdling donkeys trotting along,
Swimming sea life all day long,
And then sailing swiftly along the sea
With dancing dolphins feeling free.

The waves tickling the golden beaches
While the sea life calmly reaches.
The chip shop smells,
It's easy to tell
That you are at the seaside.

Crabs and lobsters live in the sea,
Also there they catch their tea.
Amusements galore,
You couldn't ask for any more
While you're at the seaside.

Shush quiet, shush quiet,
It's time for us to go.
It's dark now
And the tide is creeping in,
We're going home from the seaside.

Laura Foster (10)
Stoneferry Primary School

THE SEA

Swirling sand down below,
Going under with the flow.
Welcoming waves up above,
With flapping foam wrapped like a glove.

Dancing dolphins jumping out,
Seashells swaying round about.
Salty air hung round the cliffs,
And sticky stinging jellyfish.

Whales and sharks eating sea life,
Seagulls hover for a greedy fight.
A crab is crouching under a rock,
The sea is gradually coming to a stop.

All through the night it's calm and bright,
Soon it will be lit in the morning light.

Sarah Cooke (11)
Stoneferry Primary School

SEASONS TURN

The spring comes and goes,
When lambs are born and it's nice and bright.
When the spring term comes
And bank holidays approach.

The summer comes and goes
When it's nice and hot.
The children break off school
As the holidays approach.

The autumn comes and goes
When all the leaves fall,
And the children go back to school
As the holidays come to an end.

The winter comes and goes
When there's ice and snow,
And children break off for Christmas
As Christmas draws near.

Leanne Smith (11)
Stoneferry Primary School

THIS IS MY WORLD

My world is where I can be alone,
Where I can do what I like.
This is my world.

In my world I can concentrate,
Get away from my problems,
And just be normal.
This is my world.

In my world I watch TV.
In my world I play my music.
This is my world.

In my world I'm free
From my cares.
And in my world I'm
Free from my family.

This is my world.

Louise Thomas (11)
Stoneferry Primary School

MY BIRTHDAY

My birthday is so special,
A time to eat and play,
Family and friends come round for tea,
We have a wonderful day.

I have presents and cards to be opened,
And food and drink too,
Games to play, songs to sing,
I have fun all day through.

Bethany Sharp (9)
Stoneferry Primary School

WHY ME!

Why me?
I beg please don't bully me.
Why me?
It doesn't matter if I can't do what you can do.
Why me?
But I can do maths but can't do art.
Why me?
They call me four eyes just because I wear glasses.
Why me?
It doesn't matter if my mum and dad haven't got a
                                        lot of money.
Why me?
They bully me because I don't smoke.
Why me?
I say, 'I don't want to smoke' then they say, 'You're chicken.'
Why me?

Get me out of this corner.
Why me?
Don't kick me or punch me.
Why me?
I'll say this once again,
I beg *please* don't bully me.
          Why me?

Stephanie Lyth (11)
Stoneferry Primary School

THE ROLLER-COASTER

Off we go at the speed of a train,
We were dipping and slipping and swooping along,
And curling and twirling and rising and sinking,
Surprising and decreasing and screaming and screeching,
Waving and zooming and speeding and roaring,
And moaning and groaning and curling all over the place,
Moving and grooving
As the end is near,
But still shaking and dashing, also thumping and bumping,
Flashing about, crashing about and whirling and twirling,
Stop! We've finished!

Simon Johnson (10)
Stoneferry Primary School

REX

The stainless steel legs
and a head bigger than a helicopter.
A body like a tank
and eyes that are like the sun locked on a target.
It stands as big as a block of flats.

The arms are as long as a lamppost
and ears made of old metal boxes.
Deep underground it lays ready to launch
its deadly rocket filled with poisonous gas.
The warhead waits for its signal.

Jamie Morfitt (10)
Stoneferry Primary School

THE TRAMP OF HULL TOWN

He lay in the bus shelter
If it was sun shining or rain
He wore a plastic bin bag around his feet
And he wore them again and again.

People gave him things to eat,
He would say 'Hello' or 'Thank you.'
Some people would not smile,
All they would say was 'Who are you?'

One day he looked in a shop
To see all the TVs,
He said, 'I want one of those
To fit in my shelter please.'

It was dark and spooky,
He lay not harming a fly
But two kids didn't like that
And beat him up to die.

Two days later he lay in a hospital bed,
He lay so peaceful,
All his face red,
Bbbbllleeeeppp!
The tramp of Hull Town had gone!

Jenny Jones (10)
Stoneferry Primary School

MY CAT

My cat's a silly thing,
She likes to play upon my swing,
She swings it high, she swings it low,
She even swings it in a bow,
She always makes a big loud noise,
Even when she plays with boys,
She's black and white and scared at night,
But loves to play out with my kite,
She flies it high,
She flies it low,
And loves to fly it in a bow.
I love my cat,
I love her lots,
She loves to walk upon my pots,
She scrambles here,
She scrambles there,
She even scrambles on my chair,
She rubs her nose into my toes,
And always snuggles in my clothes,
She steals my rings,
And shiny things,
And thinks she has a pair of wings,
She flies so high,
She flies so low.
One day she stubbed her little toe,
She cried so loud,
She cried so low,
I had to soothe her little toe,
Then at night we'd watch TV,
With my cat Tiddles on my knee.

Frances Suzette Ellis (8)
Sutton Park Primary School

WINTER'S EVIL DANCE

Winter whispers and dances its evil dance,
The wind howls like a wolf to a glistening moon,
The snow falls on the bare branches of the isolated trees,
They shiver and moan like an old man
As he takes his final breath,
The puddles freeze like a mirror
Into a futuristic world of endless winter,
Dancing its evil dance.

Winter screeches with laughter as he finds it amusing
That he is winning the battle against summer.
Windows stare at me, hard and cold,
I place my hand upon them,
It greedily sucks the moisture from my hand,
Like a vampire draining me of my blood,
I feel I am never alone as winter surround me and follows me
Dancing its evil dance.

The winter's dark shadowy nights
Suck in the warmth of the long summer nights,
If only the moon was here to light up a path
Of hope to lead us to a brighter future,
And say farewell to winter's evil dance!

Annie Woodcock (11)
Sutton Park Primary School

LOVE

Love is knowing someone's there
To listen, to always care.
To have someone to call your own,
To know you'll never feel alone.

Marlie-Rae Willerton (9)
Sutton Park Primary School

FEATHERS

Feathers, feathers
Flutter by
As they tumble from the sky,
Very high they fluttered by.
Feathers, feathers fall and fall
Onto hard ground
Near the wall,
Flattened by one giant pound
Which was very, very round.
A big person stood on it
And just spent a little bit,
It flew back into the air
And now it's flown over there.

Katie Athorn & Louise Vernon (10)
Sutton Park Primary School

KAYLEIGH

K   ayleigh is my name
A   nd Prest is my surname
Y   ou can call me Doll if you like!
L   ove blading and riding my bike
E   xciting and energetic is what I am known for
I   also love Pooh, Piglet and Eeyore
G   ood behaviour is important
H   ealthy eater I am not.

Kayleigh Prest (8)
Sutton Park Primary School

MY TEDDY ALFIE

My teddy's name is Alfie; he always makes me laugh,
I take him everywhere I go even to the bath.
Sometimes we go shopping, sometimes we just have fun,
I buy Alfie clothes, he buys me a bun.
Summer in the garden when it's really hot,
I look after flowers while Alfie's drinking pop.
If I'm feeling frightened, or even if I'm bad,
Alfie always cuddles me to stop me feeling sad.
Then every night before we sleep, as we are laid in bed,
I look him in his eyes and say *'I love you Alfie my ted.'*

Kelly Robinson (9)
Sutton Park Primary School

SCHOOL DINNERS!

School dinners, horrible, grotty and cold.
You never get what you pay for.
The food is mouldy, the plates are greasy.
When you go and get your school dinner
The cooks give you a *cheesy* grin,
I bet they're thinking move along and *shut up!*
Even when you get your dinner it's time to go in once again
So I'm never staying for school dinners again!
        That's lots of yuck for me today!

Hannah Fennell (11)
Sutton Park Primary School

I THOUGHT . . .

I thought of a dark, lonely,
Quiet tree sitting there doing nothing
Which reminds me of an old crinkly man in an armchair.

I thought of grass frosty,
Hard, cold like being out in the evening
With nowhere to go.

I thought of a puddle
Crackling, icy,
I feel myself slipping into the puddle
I shout 'Help'

I thought of a window, cold,
Steamed up like a kettle and condensation
Streaming down the window.

I thought of a playground,
Wet, damp, insulated like a
Woman fading into a puddle of death.

Laura Green (10)
Sutton Park Primary School

WAKING UP

When I wake up in the morn
I open my eyes, stretch and have a massive yawn.

I look out of the window at my dad's newly mown lawn,
I feel so glad I was born.

Sasha Collinson (9)
Sutton Park Primary School

MY SCHOOL

I go to a little school in the middle of the sea
With the sand for my playground and pebbles beneath my feet.
We have an octopus for a teacher who lets me
Count all eight of her feet.
We play all day and then Miss will say
'Come on children we've got to go to the bay.'
Some will go home for their dinner and some have to stay,
My friends all eat seaweed for their dinner but I like waffles for mine.
Later in the day after we've been to the bay,
In the afternoon we all go to see our headmaster,
He will teach us how to swim,
Then we will all have a race and I usually win.
At half-past three I will go home for my tea
And that will be the end of the day for me.

Lee Williams (8)
Sutton Park Primary School

WINTER NIGHT

Socks keep my feet nice and warm but not in a storm.
Pins and needles, tingling toes if I go out of doors.
On a blistering night or a frozen morn,
Diamond shaped icicles cushion the floor.
Trees swaying and dancing in the wind.
Hair flying aggressively over her face,
Clothing flowing if not tightly pinned.
Rubbish is soaring all over the place.
I love to be indoors, I feel all cosy inside sat near
The fire all snug to my chair,
I always count myself lucky to be there.
People live outdoors all cold and bare.
I think all people should be indoors, it's not fair.

Laura Firth (11)
Sutton Park Primary School

THE DOOM OF THE WINTER PLAYGROUND

The cold windowpane sucked all the
heat out of my hand, like a piece of
spaghetti being slurped up by a big mouth.

When I walked on the crinkly grass,
it felt like I was walking on a crunchy
sweet in a hungry mouth.

Parts of the knobbly tree felt like an
old man's rough, wrinkly face, rubbing on
my smooth, cold hand.

The cold, smooth, slippery, iced-over
puddle looked like a cold, evil man's
heart
beating
beating
beating away in the isolated body of the playground.

The playground was as slippery as a frog's slimy nose,
waiting for the bright sun to melt the ice,
so he can get to his frozen family underneath the bundle of ice.

Sarah Capes (10)
Sutton Park Primary School

UP, UP AND AWAY

Up and up we go,
Where we'll stop nobody knows,
Spaceships, stars and the Milky Way
We'll be up there for days and days
In our shiny rocket,
I'll bring spacedust home in my pocket.

Lewis Moffat (7)
Sutton Park Primary School

PONIES

Ponies are very *big!*
They gallop all over
And do not play *tig!*

Ponies are cuddly
And furry too,
They stop quite suddenly,
Now what will they do?

Ponies are friendly,
Ponies are free,
I am wishing for one especially for me.

Ponies have a mane,
It's just like our hair,
When brushed or combed
Do they have pain?

Ponies have hooves,
They're just like our shoes,
They protect ponies feet
And our toes too.

Amy Sharpless (8)
Sutton Park Primary School

ALFIE THE TRAVELLING BEAR

Alfie the bear travels everywhere
Like Canada and America,
He rides a horse
And he hates tomato sauce,
Alfie would like to play with a ball
But he is too small.

He likes to eat meat
And he likes to smell his feet,
Alfie is a chocolate brown
And he wears a blue gown,
I am Alfie the bear
And there is not another Alfie anywhere.

When you are sad
Alfie gets mad,
When I'm alone
He talks on the phone,
While Alfie and I watch the sun go down
Alfie wishes he was a king with a crown.

Kelly Armett (9)
Sutton Park Primary School

SUMMER

Up, up in the skies above,
Birds are chasing the clouds with love.

Down, down below on the ground,
Children are dancing and singing around.

The songs that they sing
Are of summer and joy,

Summer is here,
Oh boy, oh boy.

Lauren C Brown (7)
Sutton Park Primary School

ALFIE THE BEAR

If I was Alfie the Bear
And could travel anywhere
And do anything at all
I'd think I'd have a ball.
So come closer and let me share
What it would be like to be Alfie the Bear.

I am very happy
Because I've stopped wearing my nappy.
People shout and scream
So I buy them ice-cream.
That's me Alfie the Bear
That's why all the people care.

I have been on lots of trips
But wherever I go I have to have chips.
I have climbed mountains
And down below I've seen fountains,
But now it is time for me to say goodbye,
I just thought I'd let you know that I have a tear in my eye.

Samantha Langdale (9)
Sutton Park Primary School

THE THOUGHTS OF WINTER

The tinkling rain dribbles to the ground,
The cold wind filters from the sky,
The frost hogs the fence,
And the icicles drip into the icy puddles.

The fog enters my body and makes me shiver,
The mist whirls around my head,
The whistling trees make me sing
And the frost-bitten playground makes me slip and slither.

The sound of the tinkling rain makes me sleep,
The frosty wind blows my thoughts away,
When I touch the frosty fence it makes my finger freeze,
And the brightness of the icicles make my eyes water.

I feel ticklish when the raindrops flitter on me,
I feel like a tree blowing in the wind,
The feeling of the frost makes my eyes flicker,
I feel the icicles shiver as I touch them.

I love to think about winter,
The words that are used to describe the season brings
                                    me good feelings,
We want the winter feelings to be here all the time.
The miserable weather makes me look out the window,
I feel sorry for the trees and plants in the cold whimpering weather,
I feel sorry for the animals too, in the cold moany day.

        My thoughts of winter.

Heidi Malton (10)
Sutton Park Primary School

LIFE

Life is so precious
Like a blue diamond.
People should be grateful
For what they get.
Life is so wonderful
People should try not to fret.

Life is so precious
Like a blue diamond.
People should try not to be officious
And not get into trouble.
They should tell the truth
And be as clear as a bubble.

Life is so precious
Like a blue diamond.
Women should try to be vivacious
And never be sad.
People should be good
And never be bad.

Sarah Myers (9)
Sutton Park Primary School

A SKELETON'S WISH

I wish I was a mummy
With no more rattling bones,
With bandages that cover me
From my head down to my toes.

With slits for eyes, holes for my nose,
I would creep around so quietly,
No sound, no smell, no one can tell
If I am here, if I am there,
If I am anywhere.

I sleep by day and creep by night
Giving everyone a fright.
Boo!

Katie Mattinson (9)
Tilbury Primary School

WILD FLOWERS

Look at that beautiful, wild, red rose,
Its wonderful brightness and the colour it shows.

And sunflowers, how high can they grow?
The best things about them is that they're yellow.

And look how beautiful the buttercups are,
The petals are shaped like a beautiful star.

And poppies, they're really bright red,
They all look beautiful in the flower bed.

Stephanie Cox (9)
Tilbury Primary School

THE DIVER

Soon after being sat in the warmth
I dive back down for adventure,
As I go down I see some fish,
Shiny, metallic blue swimming through an ancient hole,
I squeeze through and with a gasp
I find myself in a large ship,
The walls are frozen with white and orange barnacles,
Through my eyes I can see
A golden shine, small but clear,
It tempts me to whip around,
I can see a chest! Containing gold!
Oh no! My air is running out!
I grab five bars, rush up to the surface
And swim with glee back to shore.

Josh Daw (10)
Tilbury Primary School

SEPTEMBER

S   is for skating, it's lots of fun.
E   is for energy to help us run.
P   is for picnics, lots to eat.
T   is for tables, the sweet treats.
E   is for enjoyment, there's lots to do.
M   is for music, under skies so blue.
B   is for bikes, watch the wheels turn.
E   is for energy, watch calories burn.
R   is for relax, then go to bed thinking
     good things inside my head.

Elisha Smith (9)
Tilbury Primary School

BOYS ARE STUPID

When it snows boys hide behind walls,
But when girls are around they're not very lucky,
They get bashed and banged with snowballs,
They go screaming and crying to their mums.

Boys are fascinated by bugs,
When they lose them they leave them to die.
Mum comes in and says 'I found this bug in my rug.'
But boys are stupid they don't deny.

Boys play with army tanks,
They think tanks are great.
They pretend they rob banks,
In their own world army men are their mates.

Alicia Black (10)
Tilbury Primary School

THE ANIMAL POEM

Birds are flying to the sun,
Having so much fun.
Dogs are barking in the street,
Hear their pounding feet.

Fish are swimming in the sea
Hoping they are not for tea.
Horses jumping oh so high,
Looks like they can touch the sky.

Ashley Calver (9)
Tilbury Primary School

TREASURE HUNT

Look a whirlpool coming up to me. Help, murder, police.
Look it's taking me into that cave. I wonder what's inside?
Oh phew the whirlpool has gone,
The sea is dark in the cave.
Phew I find my torch with me.
I find a pair of keys from the deep.
What if these keys hold a secret?
Look I can't believe my eyes.
It's the great San Philips before me,
Should I go inside or back to the world?
No! I will explore this ship till my air goes out.
I'll be famous across the world.
I go inside trembling with fear.
I fall through some floorboards.
I land near a rusty door.
Could this key I hold open the door?
I put the key in the door,
It opens.
I found a skeleton on the ship.
Look she has a box in her bony hands.
I take the box and go.
I've found what I'd been looking for.
I go back up to the surface,
The familiar world.

Joseph Rowbottom (9)
Tilbury Primary School